TOLD ROUND THE PEAT FIRE

TOLD ROUND
THE PEAT FIRE

by

Andrew T. Cluness

Author of "The Shetland Isles"
(The County Book Series)

London
ROBERT HALE LTD.
63 Old Brompton Road S.W.7

First Published November 1955
Reprinted   *December* 1955
Reprinted   *August* 1958

PRINTED IN GREAT BRITAIN BY
LOWE AND BRYDONE (PRINTERS) LIMITED, LONDON, N.W.10

CONTENTS

PREFACE

The long happy nights of yarns by the peat fires have gone; the radio and other distractions of a mechanised age have come. Soon we may even have television and then— "Thy hand, great Anarch, lets the curtain fall!" The old people are rapidly passing away, the very peat fires themselves are becoming fewer, and the stream of young life ebbs from the islands to the crowded centres of civilisation, from which in due time the hydrogen bomb may splash them back again.

And with the very old there passes away a wonderful store of tales and legends once more inexhaustible and varied than those of Scheherazade, tales with which our fore-fathers beguiled the long winter nights, and the longer and sometimes wearier days and nights of continuous fishing in their little open boats far out at sea.

This collection of yarns and old legends, largely from one little island, the most northerly in Britain, is as the St. Paul Rocks in mid-Atlantic, a few bare peaks, emerging above the waves, of a vast submerged continent of narrative now forgotten for evermore. Time deals hardly with legend. So faint now is the memory of Goturm's Hole and Yela Brun and Glatna Kirk that the writer felt that if some attempt were not now made to make their stories permanent, or at least more lasting, such an effort would never be made. The Helga legend of more recent date is of course still remembered in greater detail but the memory of it too is fading and it is too good a story to be allowed to be forgotten.

Apart from the legends, the other tales, now loosely strung together, were narrated as facts, generally within the personal experience of the narrator. But the reader must judge for himself. From personal knowledge of some at least of the story tellers, this warning may be given. While they could make what was untrue assume the appearance of truth, they delighted yet more in adorning the truth until it seemed untrue.

Two short extracts, one from the *Wreck of the Harvest Rose*, and the other from *There She Blows*, have already appeared in the *New Shetlander*.

1

"THERE SHE BLOWS!"

OUTSIDE the little cottage the north wind laden with snow roared gustily in sullen muffled tones, and rumbled in the chimney; but within, the peat fire diffused from its friendly blaze a more than ample warmth. We were comfortable. So far advanced along life's circle was the old man that now the days of his youth were closer to his recollection than the long stretch of manhood with all its activities and external contacts. Now "snug shorded by his ain hearth-stone" he puffed gratefully at his foul old pipe and in relaxed mood called back to memory days long forgotten save by himself. He remembered the snows of eighty years agone more vividly than the gales and frosts of the previous winter; he remembered a golden age when the weather was far more of a piece than it is now, when summer was one long glorious stretch of fine weather, and when in winter the snowdrifts piled up about the steading so that a trench had to be dug between house and byre, and between house and well. Yes, snow was snow in his young days.

"Tammas o' Taft had gone from Muness to Oesund to the shop on a snowy day, and when he set out on the return journey night had already fallen and a vast blinding snowstorm from the north-east blew in his face. But he didn't mind. His stout staff made a third leg as it were, and keeping wind and snow in his face he plodded stoutly on. It was in the days before the road was laid of course and he had a full three miles to go. He knew where he was

until he reached the Brake of Clivocast, but thereafter had
to go by guess.

"A nasty stretch of ground lay before him, along by the
Brake and through the mires of Rindaleog with its peat
banks and burns. Soon he began to be uncertain of his
way but on and on he went. Many a time when he thrust
his staff before him into the snow he found no bottom, and,
judging that he must be on the edge of a peat bank, he
felt his way cautiously to firmer ground where the snow was
less deep. Soon he was plunging up to and over the knees
at every step and began to realise he was using up his
strength too quickly—he must go slowly and he must keep
going. Deeper and deeper became the snow; he was above
his waist now, and then he found firmer footing on what
seemed a little hillock.

"He stopped, partly it may be in exhaustion but far
more in amazement, for he was looking down through a
hole in the snow from which came a bright glow and the
sound of voices. When he stooped and looked this way and
that through the hole he recognised the folk of Litla-
garth—they were drying corn in a big kettle and he was
standing on their barn roof!

"Well, well, soon he was inside the house among them
and they made him welcome and insisted that he should
stay the night; for he was far from his course, and still had
half the distance to go, and although it had ceased to snow,
conditions were just impossible.

"Next day after very hard frost during the night the
people were out and about tending to the animals and
young Andrew coming in said:

"Tammas, just come out a bit and see where you were
last night!"

"Tammas followed him and his own tracks back for a
quarter of a mile or so. They led to the top of the cliffs
at the Neap and there Tammas could see where he had
passed along the very verge of the hundred feet drop and

his staff had bored holes through the snow overhanging
the very edge!"

But here the old man checked himself, and, with a
twinkle in his bright black eyes peering out from beneath
the projecting grey bushes of his eyebrows and with his
sharp hawk nose thrust forward, said:

"But never mind about the snow! Did you do what I
told you about the whales?"

I assured him I had done so and he settled himself more
comfortably in his big straight-back Orkney chair and
puffing away said:

"Well, let's hear it!"

Now it had happened that on my previous visit we had
been discussing very ancient times indeed. He had an
enormous admiration for the Israelites especially for such
men as Samson and Samuel and Benaiah the son of Jehoi-
ada and such like—men who had their ruthless berserk
moments. On the other hand the Greeks and the Romans
were to him contemptible, and the Egyptians and Assyrians
altogether past speaking about. The only men that could
in his opinion match the Chosen Race were the men of his
own youth who had waged war hand to hand so to speak
against the whales in Davis Straits, and laid low the polar
bears on the grinding ice floes in Greenland's fjords. When
I had tentatively averred that the ancients, some of them
(not the Jews) were equally well skilled in whale hunting he
would not have that to be at all; for one thing there were no
men who could handle small boats well enough in those
days. I said I knew of two stories in books I had read that
proved my point. He wished me to bring the books next
time I called and I promised I would bring a translation at
any rate. So indeed here I was all prepared with an account
written in an exercise book.

He listened appreciatively while I read slowly the following account of how whales were caught by men of ancient
days.

"All whales are slow in swimming and do not proceed without some little fish to guide them. This guide shows them everything, whether booty to catch, or any danger near, or neighbouring shallows, and they obey it at the flick of its tail; by it they hear and see, nor is their own strength of such value to the huge monsters as the cleverness of the tiny fish.

"Wherefore the wily fisher, to be able to take monsters of this kind, first of all with various and manifold allurements of bait catches this fish and then without difficulty takes the monsters; for bereft of their guide they no longer perceive their path in the sea, nor are aware of imminent danger, but wander at random, mere vast bulks, borne any whither by the waves. For bereft of their guide, and with a fleshy mass projecting over their eyes their vision is obscured in darkness, and they dash against the rocks and shore.

"Then the fishermen discuss the taking of one of these monsters but first of all they guess at its size and weight. For if its head projects a little above the water that is a clear indication that it is a huge monster; if its back is well above water it is not so big, for the smaller, as they are lighter, show so much the more above the surface.

"The fishers make a cable twisted of many ropes, in thickness like the stay such as holds fast the mast of a fair-sized ship at either end from stem to stern. To this they add an iron chain which they attach to a hook, lest it should be chafed by the monster's teeth. They make the hook large, as big as can conveniently be seized in the monster's jaws, and strong as a rock. In the chain itself there are many loops to restrain the enraged movements of the beast lest it should break the iron in its contortions, for they writhe around so that the chain does not remain in one position.

"Their bait is the liver or shoulder of a bull. Many of the fishers join together in the work. They have ready at hand lances, harpoons or sickles, axes and other suchlike weapons fashioned by smiths on the anvil.

"Then rowing in silence they indicate by a nod if anything is required, and take the utmost care that the whale does not through hearing any sound seek refuge in the deep. When they are now near they let down the bait from the prow and present it to the monster.

"When he sees the bait, without any delay he seizes it with unbridled greed and immediately his throat is pierced by the hook. Roused by the pain he tries to gnaw and destroy the chain, and after he has tried this for a long time with great effort, stung with grievous pains he plunges into the depths of the sea. Then they slack out to him all the rope, as he could not be drawn back by any human strength and could easily in his madness draw down boat and rowers into the deep. At the same time they attach by lines large wind-filled skins when the whale dives. Goaded by the pain of his wound he despises the skins and drags them struggling and ever seeking the surface down to the depths of the sea. When he reaches the very bottom he rests exhausted and breathes out great billows.

"But the inflated skins do not suffer him to rest, much as he desires to, raising him again to the surface. So he renews and resumes his strife against them, and as though they were living creatures his enemies, he pursues them in his desire for revenge, and again and again drags the skins this way and that way in vain; they, bobbing about, ever evade him. In great pain once more he seeks the depths, and moves sometimes at his own will sometimes by the external strain, and rages so mightily and raises such watery storms that you might think Borcas had his abode beneath the waves.

"Then some of the fishers rowing straight to shore fasten the rope to a rock and return to the sea. At last when the monster is exhausted and his strength now spent, some skin-bag bobs to the surface as a messenger of victory; soon the rest appear too, and with them the whale even against his will is drawn; so the fishers gather round in their boats and encouraging each other as though in battle, with great enthusiasm and great noise assail the beast. Some with spears and javelins, some with tridents, others armed with axes, sickles and other weapons slash him however he struggles and whatever storms he raises with his blowing, and into his wounds from which he reddens the sea they pour rotten bilge-water, sharp and biting like fire.

"When he is finally overcome they draw him to the shore and on to the beach where he now dying quivers in vain, and feebly moves his fins and breathes deeply. And in this manner very large whales are taken. The capture of smaller whales is easier and the apparatus as might be expected on a smaller scale—a hook, bait and line, and instead of goatskin bags gourds are used."

The Ancient had listened with a mixture of incredulity and admiration. When I concluded he laughed and being very outspoken said that he scarcely believed one word of it.

"Please yourself about believing it; it certainly isn't my lie. The man who wrote the account was called Oppianus. He was a Greek who wrote a treatise on Fishing and he lived nearly *eighteen hundred years ago*."

"But there are no whales in the Mediterranean!"

"No, they were in the Indian Ocean; there were plenty of them there, for when Alexander the Great's fleet sailed there, the Macedonians related that they encountered many whales of incredible size so that they were terrified and lost all hope of their lives, for they expected to be devoured, ships and all. But plucking up courage they all simultaneously clashed their arms and sounded their trumpets and the monsters terrified plunged beneath the sea."

I might have spared my display of erudition; he was not listening.

"Fishing," said he, as if he were stunned, "fishing for

whales with a bull's liver for bait, mainmast stays for a line, and skinbuoys for floats! I don't believe it. And even if such a thing ever happened, it must have taken them days to catch one whale. Two in one day was the best catch I ever saw made, though in 'Sixty-one Jamie o' Noostigirt's ship the *Nautilis* caught five in one day."

"Five!" said I, "that wasn't any great fishing; nothing surprising in that! Just you listen to this!"

Referring to the exercise book once more I remarked by way of preface. "Now this didn't happen in 'Sixty-one but more than a *thousand years ago*. Ohere the sailor told King Alfred of England that he lived very far north in Norway; that his own land was the best hunting ground for whales; and that he and five others had killed *sixty whales in two days*! Now what about Jamie o' Noostigirt?"

"Sixty in two days—man I wonder at you, believing stuff like that!"

"It's written here."

"Oh, well, it must have been the small caaing whales that used to come here years ago."

"No, it wasn't; he takes care to say that the whales he is talking about were generally seventy feet long and the largest seventy-five feet."

"Do you mean to tell me that six men killed sixty whales all seventy foot long in two days? Na, na, I take it that yon man what's-his-name was as big a liar as Tommy Dinnly! How could they do it?"

"Do you know I'm inclined to think his story is true. He gives a long account of a voyage of discovery he made. He was probably the first man to sail round the North Cape as far as the White Sea, and gives what is admitted to be a very accurate account of such a voyage. His account too of the size of the whales rings true. Perhaps they chased them over a sandbank with the flood-tide into a narrow creek and then killed them at their leisure. Something like that may have happened."

He reflected in silence refilled his pipe and stroked his beard.

"Well, I'm not believing a word of what you've told me. (If any reader has similar doubts he is referred to the appendix!) I have heard of only one whale being caught that way—the whale Daa Jockie killed in the Muckle Gio o' Balta."

I slipped the exercise book into my pocket—it had served its purpose.

"You've been in Balta Isle and know the Muckle Gio of course. I've been there only once myself and one look down the steep face of the cliff was enough for me but for Jockie it had no terrors. He was a great man for going in search of wreckwood and one summer day what did he see right up at the end of the Gio but an enormous whale. It had come in so far and was so large that it hadn't turning room and was wallowing and floundering about. Jockie climbed down and waded into the sea to his middle to get alongside the great head. With his gully he began cutting in through the blubber. The whale splashed and rolled and puffed, threshed with its great tail raising waves so that the spray was at times over Jockie's head, but the tide was on the ebb and it stuck fast.

"Jockie was drenched to the hide but grimly continued his task. He had dug a hole until his arms were over the elbows in the blubber before he drew blood and then he stabbed vigorously until the blood streamed. The whale, poor brute, is so made by the hand of the Almighty that once it begins to lose blood there's no stopping till it dies. Jockie now left it, climbed the cliff again, went down the slope to his boat and rowed across to Baltasound for men to help in flensing it. By the time a boat's crew had rowed round the whale was dead. They got a vast quantity of blubber from it, and in time its jawbones were stuck up in front of the big house in Baltasound to form a great archway. I've heard men say they were twenty-seven feet long. The gully Jockie killed it with is still in existence.

"That was the only time I ever heard of a man accounting for a whale singlehanded, but there was once I had a chance of doing it myself!

"Indeed I did. I mind when I was a boy of about twenty we used to have great dellings and we would come from roundabout to somebody's croft seven or eight or maybe a dozen of us and 'dell' for soul and body until night. And I mind I had a brand new spade-haft, and, thinks I, I'll make sure that no one takes away my spade by *mistake* (for you'll notice it's never an old spade or an old oar that's ever taken by *mistake*). So I had sat down, and with the help of a bit of heated wire, had burned my initials on the haft.

"Well, I had the spade at a few dellings and one fine voar morning I was going to a great delling at the Gios—I was coming down past Smirgirt, and had just come above the sands when I saw a great black monster of a thing lying about the middle of them below Hooligirt. When I came close what should it be but a great whale. He had come in too near and his head was grounded on the beach. What size was he? Sixty feet if he was an inch, and there was I with nothing but a spade, and not a soul in sight to send for a lance or a harpoon. For of course it was the time of the whaling days and we had both harpoons and men that could handle them.

"But I did have the new spade and I walked boldly up and drove it as hard as I could into his head. I mind me noticing the little wicked eyes of him and then—he gave one wallop with his tail, and I was flat on my back with a shower of sand and water in my face harder than any hail I ever felt.

"When I got to my feet, and had cleared my eyes of water and sand, there was my spade sticking up like the mast of a waterlogged sixern about the length of two boughts of lines from the shore: but there wasn't much waterlogged about the speed it was travelling at. It was going like a steamer

B

straight between the Vair and Huney. I watched as long as I could see him but he never altered course and so went my spade-haft."

He was silent and thoughtful for a time. After the lapse of more than seventy years the loss could still move him to sorrowful contemplation.

"Well, well," he started off again. "When I got to the Gios the young folk were already going down from the house to the taatie rig and someone says:

'Come on, you've slept in this morning.'

"When I came up, Johnnie Tamson says:

" 'Where's your spade, Tammie?'

" 'Where's my spade?' says I, 'by this time he's fifty miles benorth o' Balta!' And when I told them my story they laughed and laughed, and all that day every now and then old Magnie would slap a clod with his spade and say: 'Fifty miles benorth o' Balta,' and young Andrew o' Sanook would say, 'It's a mercy you had your initials on him!'

"But it's a wise man that knows how anything he makes will turn out, or what will be the end of it. The summer after that, a lot of the young men were at the Greenland whaling. It was the year before I went myself, and when they came back about the end of October they had plenty of stories to tell. Young Andrew o' Sanook had been among them and the first night he was home he came along and dumped down a lot of things he was carrying.

"We were glad to get all the news and talked away for a bit, and then he began to laugh.

" 'Man, Tammie, I've a great tale to tell you for you come into the story too. One morning there were four or five ships of us sailing close to the land. I was in the crow's nest and saw a spout of a whale about three miles astern, and bawled out: "Blo-o-o-w, there's she blows" with all my might. It meant four pounds of baccy for the man who saw the whale first—if we got him. In no time the ship was put about, and when we were half a mile or so away, our four boats were out and after him. Before we came near him another rose just before the chief mate's boat.

"'I was with the second mate a bit astern, and we saw them fast in no time.

" 'Row, for heaven's sake, row,' sings out our mate. He had noticed that a boat from another ship, the *Alert*, was making for our whale. But by Providence he turned a bit our way and we were close up as soon as they were. Lowrie Bruce hurled his harpoon at him just as a harpoon from the other boat came swishing over his back, and struck the water within an oar's length of our boat.

"'And we were fast! Away he went, the line spinning out in coils and jumping like a living thing. By and by he sounded and took out two tubs of lines before he came up again. We, hauling on the line, in the end got close to him, lanced him, and in half an hour he was dead. The first mate's boat by this time had their whale in tow—so we did well yon day—two sixty foot whales.

"'And here's the bit you'll not believe! When we came to the ship's side and began flensing, we found sticking in his neck what looked like a bit of a wooden pole, and what think you was it when we cut it out. Nothing more nor less but your spade!'"

"'No,'" said I, "'that I'll not believe.'"

" 'Well,' says he, 'seeing is believing,' and with that he got up, went out towards the door and taking up one of his packages unwrapped the very spade I had thought was gone for evermore. The blade was worn thin and the top part of the haft covered with littel round barnacles. But it was my own identical spade with my own initials burned into it."

He was silent for a time. Then he added: "And Andrew handed me two pounds o' baccy, for as he said if it hadn't been for me he might never have seen the whale. Baccy was cheap in those days."

He bent forward and busied himself adjusting the blazing

peats still nearer to the heart's desire. Continuing to grasp the tongs he pointed: "See you yon straight blazing brand over at your cheek of the fire. We're going to have a visitor."

Without the aid of pyromancy the dog Sloppy had already become aware of the fact and rising languidly sauntered towards the door, moving his tail so slowly from side to side that wagging is a frivolous term to apply to such a dignified action.

The visitor was a welcome one to us both—the old man's neighbour, himself now beginning to a slight degree to stoop under the burden of years. He could still, however, at seventy, put in a solid day's work of fifteen hours or so, six days a week, and would have felt uncomfortable with less to do. He had raised a large family and could laugh more heartily than any of them, for in addition to tolerance he had a great gift for seeing the whimsical and humorous side of things. His fund of tales was large and his somewhat unusual angle of approach made the truth (for he generally told the truth) seem like something untrue.

After the usual interchange of talk about the snow, sheep, and the possible shortage of fodder, if the new moon failed to bring a change, the Ancient said.

"The boy here has been reading to me about six men who killed sixty whales, seventy foot long every one of them, in two days, and about another lot who used an iron hook baited with a bull's liver and a line like a ship's cable to fish for whales. He says it's history. Have you ever read or heard of such arrant nonsense?"

John threw back his head and laughed gloriously, his grey beard shaking. Alas, alas! Among other things we have lost is the gift of laughter, full and strong and unquenchable as the old gods of Olympus and Asgard knew it!

When at last his rumblings died away he sat erect and commented:

"Well, well, I mind my granny used to tell us about the

two giants Herman and Saxi that lived in old ancient times in the north end of the isle. She did say that Herman used to fish for whales just as we fish for sillocks—only he used the main mast of a three-masted ship for a rod and a fat sheep for bait! I aye used to think that was just her nonsense but if this story in the history books is true, her story maybe held a grain of truth too.

"As for the sixty whales in two days—I have seen as many as that driven ashore here in one morning. But the truth is they were not seventy feet long—there's no use telling lies about it—the deil one of them was seventy feet— the biggest might have been twenty at the outside. You mind well enough about that yourself—the *Maid of the Sea* and the *Calm Summer*?"

"Yes, yes," said the old man appealed to, hunching his shoulders and holding out his long thin hands to the blaze— "but tell you the story yourself. It'll likely no lose anything in the telling," and he grinned in friendly fashion.

"It began on a fine Sunday morning. I was about twelve years old at the time and some of us were going very sedately along the beach to the kirk, when Jamie o' the Mill who was plodding very seriously and soberly beside his wife and young Donald his son and my special chum, stopped suddenly and cried: 'The whales, boys, the whales!' His wife looked at him in reproof, but he was gazing out the voe and so were we. And he was right!

"Round the westward point of Uyea you could see the calm waters rent and broken by the rounded backs and fins, and now and then a head would remain sticking up a little, the waters disturbed in a turmoil for hundreds of yards around!

"It was a sore temptation indeed, for yonder were whales sufficient to bring in a good sum of money to every man on the beach if we could get them ashore. We stood and stood until Mary said:

" 'So, come, we're late for the kirk.'

"The minister, when we got there, had seen what was the matter, for we weren't the only ones who were late. Little escaped his notice and he took as his text 'Remember the Sabbath day'. He *could* preach, nothing milk and water about his sermons at any time and he excelled himself that day!

"But in spite of his lurid warnings, such is human nature that as soon as we were out of the kirk every eye was turned on the whales—hundreds and hundreds of them. They had come in past Musselbroch and were circling and playing about not three hundred yards from the shore, the sun shining brightly on their glossy backs, the bigger ones circling sleekly round the school like dogs round a flock of sheep. Such a drove had not been seen for years and of all days they had to come on a Sunday, when not the worst outcast in the village would dare to launch a boat for the purpose of catching them. Even so, most of the men after dinner strolled down to the boats and saw that they were ready. Midnight would come sometime and there was no harm in being ready.

"It was the longest afternoon and evening I have ever known. Men would pass backwards and forwards uneasily and speak shortly to each other but no man mentioned whales. One here and there would slip quietly away and furbish up old harpoons and flensing knives until their wives checked them. Then they would restlessly return to pace the beach once more.

"And then about seven o'clock a tragedy happened, caused as might be expected by godless strangers. There was an English ship in the harbour—the *Maid of the Sea* from Runcorn. She had just discharged a cargo of salt and was on the point of sailing away, and the poor benighted atheists aboard of her had nothing better to do on a Sunday evening than to launch their dinghy and go splashing and shouting among the whales.

"There was for a little the silence of a great horror, and

then you should have heard the yells raised by every man, woman, and bairn on the beach. If we could have got hold of that boat's crew they would have been torn in pieces. As it was, old Robbie of Clivocast, who had lost a leg in the navy, rushed into the sea with an old harpoon he was absentmindedly carrying, and—Sabbath day though it was —poured out such a string of deep-sea profanity as had not before been heard by anyone. But it was too late! The whales had taken fright and in ten minutes the last of them disappeared round the westward end of the Isle. The ship's boat, fortunately for its occupants, returned to the *Maid of the Sea*.

"We had a quiet supper that night. Father was in an evil mood, and Mother hushed us away to bed like chickens, and next morning the men set out as usual in their sixerns for the deep-sea fishing grounds. Given good fishing they might be back on Thursday but more likely it would be Saturday. Our lot was little happier—we had to go to school and submit in that prison to the voice and blows of an impatient tyrant.

"Fine I remember that morning. He had got round to the Catechism lesson and pounced on me.

" 'Boy, what is effectual calling?'

"I didn't know, but in an instant he did, for Willie of Brookpoint who sat next the window suddenly gave a yell: 'Boys, the whales!' and rushed for the door. In one minute all the boys and half the girls were outside; and in less than two the teacher with the rest. The minister might keep us ashore on Sunday, but no power on earth could hold us on a weekday.

"We rushed to the beach, seized every boat there was, piled in a heap of stones for ammunition and off we went, boys and girls, every boat crowded. In the excitement, McDougal the teacher had forgot to put the plug in his boat and had to turn back with his crew when they found the boat filling. When I tell you we didn't even laugh when we realised what had happened you can see how excited we were. We could see all the boats coming off from the Westside too, the women screaming and splashing their oars, and out from the cottages behind us thronged all who could walk and yelled at us to come back and take them on board.

"But we held on, all except the teacher's crew, and very proud we were for we had the commander on board, old Robbie of Clivocast, who had been down at the beach, wooden leg, harpoon and all, as soon as any of us. He took charge right away, made us form a line and close the Skuda Sound; the Westside boats too were now strung out across the Wester Sound, in charge of Inga, a great gaunt rawboned shrew whose voice and exhortations were second only to Robbie's.

"Soon the wings of the fleet joined and slowly we drove the whales towards the beach. Hurling stones and shouting until our throats were dry we drove them on. Sometimes one would rise quite close and with a snort vanish again. Little jets of spray hung in a haze over the surface of the water; between us and the shore the sea was in a turmoil worse than Bluemull Sound on a windy day. The bigger whales, rushing round on the outskirts at astonishing speed, would try to shepherd the school seawards but always we headed them off. Two crews had by this time come up from Uyea and were formed into a rearguard by Robbie to head off any whales that broke through the line. Even the *Maid of the Sea* sent a boat, which either from inclination or fear of Robbie's outspoken comments on their seamanship, joined the Uyea boats and shouted and splashed to their heart's content.

"Nearer and nearer to the shore we drove the seething mass, the big bulls tearing through the waters distracted, and the mothers with the little ones close under their fins, like arms thrown out to protect them. The biggest bull of all, at last maddened by the noise and hail of stones, rushed straight on to the beach with a kind of squeak of relief and in a moment the beach was awelter with the glistening bodies, black above, greyish white beneath. Robbie was in the water up to the waist, waded ashore and the slaughter began.

"It was horrible but exciting. Two men would rush into the sea, grasp hold of the fins, one on either side, draw the smooth body a bit towards shore. Then Robbie or some other harpooner would thrust his weapon under the raised fin to the creature's heart. It would lie motionless for a little, then quiver and lash the water with its tail, again lie still for a time, then struggle feebly and more feebly till it died. The sea was red with blood when at the end of the day we had two hundred and sixty-seven of them dragged above high-water mark—the largest close on eighteen feet, the smallest less than six. Men said there had not been such a drove for forty years.

"There was no school for any of us for days. The work of flensing kept us busy, as all the able-bodied men were at sea. Hard work it was and still unfinished when on Friday the fishermen returned. While waiting for a favourable wind the skipper of the *Maid of the Sea* and his crew took an active part in the flensing, but an unfortunate accident had befallen the former. He had lost his footing on the slippery beach and gashed his thigh rather badly on a rusty harpoon. He was taken to the Mill but was considered too hurt to be removed for a time.

"Saturday came and with the help of some of the fishermen the end of our task. They had naturally been delighted when they returned. They said they could see the cloud of gulls hovering when they were miles away. We had no place on the beach to store the blubber so that it was heaped together and covered to some extent with tarpaulins and old sails, and stones laid thereon. The carcases of the whales lay on the beach as yet, for they had to be officially measured.

"Now our troubles began. By law the spoil had to be divided into three portions in the presence of the Fiscal. One part belonged under certain circumstances to the Admiral (who he was I never knew), one part to the proprietor of the land on which the whales had come ashore, and one part to those who had driven them there; while the minister was entitled to a tithe of the whole.

"The Baillie of the parish, Tammas of Norderhus had to be called and there were cheers when he said the Admiral could not claim any part as every whale there was small enough to be drawn by four oxen. That was the rule. He had sent to Lerwick for the Fiscal. Well, it was Friday before he came and at once he declared that the spoil should be equally divided between the proprietors of the beach on the one hand and ourselves on the other—except of course for the minister's tithe if he claimed it. There was no if about it though, for the Reverend John was as good a business man during the week as he was a minister on Sunday.

"But as bad luck would have it the beach belonged to two proprietors and some of the whales had come ashore on one side of the division mark, some on the other. The proprietors couldn't agree; one demanded a half in all the whales that had come ashore on his property, the other stuck out for a division in proportion to the length of space belonging to each between the two whales farthest apart. Each claimed of course what suited him best and neither would listen to the Baillie's suggestion about equal shares. When the Baillie and Fiscal together decided it so, they pleased neither party.

"But they were not the only ones to be displeased. You can imagine the rage of us bigger boys when we were one and all classed as 'children' and Inga and the women and even the crew of the *Maid of the Sea* as 'grown ups'. Fancy! I got the same share as wee Kirsty Anderson, seven years old, who had sat and wept in our boat all the time and had pleaded with us to 'let them be' and had run away weeping when we came ashore! And still worse the Englishmen who hardly knew one end of an oar from the other got as grown-ups twice our share. But it was no use grumbling. Mc-Dougal strutted up and down with the school list in his hand. He knew who were at school and who not. And, mind you, he got a full share, the man who didn't know enough about a boat to put in the plug!

"Now another difficulty arose. We had no barrels in which to put the blubber, for this was before the days of the great herring fishings. But Captain Parret of the *Maid of the Sea* sent word for it to be shipped just as it was aboard his ship. He anticipated a quick run and a little whale oil would not harm his hold, only make his ship the tighter.

"In a few days it was all aboard, and with Thursday's high tide we boys amused ourselves in thrusting off the carcases from the beach and watching them drift, each surrounded by an oily patch of calm water, and all accompanied by its cloud of gulls, quietly before the wind south towards Fetlar and Yell.

"But a week again elapsed before the captain was helped on board, for his wound had proved slow in healing, and it was now nearly three weeks since the whale hunt. Fate surely was against him. As the old wives say: 'It had to be!' For ten days from that day we had a gale, first from the north, then from the south-east, such that at times the ship was in danger of dragging her anchors. That was followed by the 'Long Calm', a calm such as we have never in all my minding had since.

"At the end of the gale the crew had come ashore for provisions and water, happy at the idea of sailing the following day. In a few days they came ashore again saying they thought it would be more pleasant to stay there until they could set out. Three days later the ship's presence was felt ashore even if one were not at the water's edge, and after *ten* days of perfectly calm hot weather no one cared to go even to the shore if it could be avoided. Some daring souls who had rowed up close to the ship saw that the bulwarks and even a little of the lower rigging were beginning to be coated with a greyish white!

"Day after day of windless scorching brightness and night after night of cloudless sky. June came to an end and still the calm continued; now for more than four weeks it had lasted, and miles away that ship made her presence known! By this time every bit of her above water was a white living crust and the tons of rotting stuff in her hold sent out its ghastly breath. Great fins of sharks drawn from hundreds of miles away circled round and round her. The smaller fish had been scared from their wonted haunts. She seemed to have killed the very air for even the growing crops wilted and drooped!

"It was evident something must be done. The captain and crew were ordered to take their ship away, and finally they were compelled to board their dinghy and were thrust off from the shore. They rowed close to the ship, but turned at the last moment and rowed quickly away crying out that it was impossible.

"Finally when in desperation the principal laird offered a cow to any man who would board her and knock out the shackles of the anchor chains so that she could be towed away, Andrew Ohlson, who used to boast he could do anything, went out with a crew of daredevils and got on board. He knew his job and succeeded before plunging overboard. There was not much breath in him when he was picked up, and his crew rowed out of range where he slowly recovered.

"But his task was done. Soon they had a rope made fast to the jib-boom stay, and slacking out they began to tow the *Maid of the Sea* slowly away. It was hard work but they soon had helpers. Boat after boat put out, more and more ropes were bent on to the towline, and, through the oily calm which now seemed to have existed always, she forged ahead.

"Out they went, the whole village it seemed either in the boats or standing by the cottage doors agaze at the passing of their hopes which had turned to worse than ashes. Out into the Pool, the space of open water round which lay dreaming and reflected upside down, Unst and Fetlar, Yell and Uyea, and the little islets.

"There in the centre she came to a pause when it was noticed several boats were coming up from Fetlar and Yell on the port and starboard bows, coming in silent menace to repel by violence if necessary any nearer approach. A short distance away they rested on their oars, and the admiral of the Yell contingent dared them to come nearer. They had had to endure the drifting 'crangs' of their adjectival whales, but he would be submerged and uncomfortably obliterated (or words to that effect) if they would tolerate their rotten blubber! So for a little the fleets rested on their oars, all eyes upon the ship, all fully aware of her overmastering presence. A cry of a sudden burst from a dozen throats 'She's going down!'

"And so she was. The abrupt jerking of the towrope had done what was necessary and in a few minutes without a sound she slipped beneath the still surface of the water leaving scarcely a ripple, and in silence the boats turned away to their respective shores."

The narrator was silent for a little, sucking at an empty pipe, and then by way of epilogue went on:

"Curious how things come about! It was noticed not long after that fish could be got in abundance over the spot where she went down. Aye, I know it well—the rift in the Hog o' Strandabroch bearing over the east corner of the Clett, and Wedderholm just touching the south end of Haaf Gruney. By and by men began to call this spot the 'White Ship'."

"Imphm," said the Ancient, "many a good codling I've

drawn there. But there's no saying what comes into your mind when you begin talking about whales! It's not the usual but the unusual that somehow sticks.

"I never had any experience myself out of the ordinary at the actual Greenland whaling, though I was there for three years, and yet Seemon o' the Knowes on his very first voyage was in no less than three ships before he returned. His first struck an iceberg and the crew had to abandon ship. They were picked up by another whaler which in turn was nipped and finally crushed in the ice itself. So he came home on ship number three.

"He said the thing he best remembered was an incident that happened after they were ordered to abandon the second ship. Everything that could be of service to them was of course taken from the whaler and stacked together on the ice but in the final flurry and hurry a rum-cask fell from the sling and split. So the rum was lost or appeared to be so.

"But one of the bold lads was nimble enough to pull off one of his long seaboots and scooped it nearly full of the liquor, and went round hopping for a time on one foot, and holding the seaboot as carefully as if it were a baby. His chums laughed at him at first, but not so long afterwards he was comfortable enough for he was selling his rum! The price was tuppence a glass and the three hours' loan of a seaboot that fitted the vendor!

"That seemed to Seemon the oddest thing he saw on this first troubled voyage of his but he told me a story that I found still more strange. And it's quite a true story too!

"There were two Yell men in the crew. I forget their names—not that it matters—the thing could have happened to anybody and it did happen to them. We can call them Sam and Bob for the time being.

"Now these two were grand lads with their hands, and while some of the others after the first day on the ice found time hanging heavily they occupied their leisure time in hollowing out and fashioning into shape a small bit of broken spar they had divided between them. What do you think each was making? What else but a little model Shetland smack. It was only when the hulls were completed, the lead keels attached, and the masts and rigging in position, that the other men paid much attention. Certainly when they stood at last all complete with mainsail, foresail, jib, neat and trim, they were worth seeing. From comment on their lines and the cut of their sails the other men began to argue as to which was the better boat and bets were laid and taken about their sailing capabilities.

"But Sam and Bob were reluctant to hazard their own and their boats' reputations before making final adjustments, of sail balance, mast position and slope, rudder areas, and Heaven knows what all! They both agreed that 'bairns and fules should never see work half done' and mutually resolved to test their handiwork privately before making a public display.

"So one fine morning off they set over the ice in search of a suitable pool. At last when about a mile from the ship, (which though crushed was still held fast) and almost out of sight of it, they found what they wanted. In the ice was an almost round little loch about two hundred yards across. Near to it at one place the ice had packed and built up in a short ridge with its highest hummocks eight or ten feet above the surrounding level, leaving a narrow space between it and the water's edge. The two boats were placed a few yards apart and then together Sam's *Jessie* and Bob's *Mary* were started off on the port tack heading fairly close into the breeze which was just sufficient to ripple the pool.

"For a glorious hour forgotten almost entirely were their surroundings. The sun shone his brightest, swinging low in a clear sky, striking flashes of emerald from the ice hummocks, and making a dazzle of glistening white on the surrounding snow. They saw it not; their eyes were on the bobbing leaping boats—their minds as happy as when they had sailed their little boats on Lunga Water or Lumbister Loch.

"They were truly happy but a serpent entered their Eden too. Sam was now on the far side of the loch close beside the ice ridge as the *Jessie* came to land. He bent down to alter her sheets and steering gear. As he did so he heard Bob approach, and without looking up said: 'I'll gie her a bit mair wadderhelm.' Bob just grunted, and Sam, after attending to this matter added: 'And slacken the jib sheet just a kenning.' Bob grunted again but so vigorously that Sam, pushing off his boat, looked up in surprise. He found himself facing at a distance of six feet or so a polar bear rearing up on its hind legs to a height of seven feet! It's red throat gaped in what seemed a fantastic grin of anticipation!

"Sam stood rooted to the spot paralysed. He saw only the vast form and the dreadful leering face. Fortunately for him the bear's attention was for a moment divided and distracted. There were Bob's shouts of exhortation to his chum to run for Heaven's sake, there was the strange dancing, bobbing bird (the *Jessie* plunging and reaching to windward), and last of all a little poke at his left hind paw. The *Mary* had completed her course too late to overtake the *Jessie* but providentially enough to thrust her little jib-boom far enough forward over the ice to touch him. Here was another of the strange white winged birds pertly bobbing and pecking at him! The bear stooped lithely, its forepaw swooped catlike, and mainsail, jib, foresail, mast and rigging of the poor *Mary* fluttered in his paw. He turned the tangle of broken gear this way and that, then bent and struck again, and the hull leaped out of the water and lay at his feet.

"Needless to say Sam had not waited but was off along the loch like the wind, running his soul out towards the ship. But as he ran his mind began to work again. Long before he could cover the mile that lay between him and safety the bear would catch him. Bob would have to help him! He continued therefore to follow the edge of the water.

"Bob's first idea too after shouting had also been to run away. But when he saw his *Mary* over which he had spent so many anxious but happy hours so rudely handled, its rigging torn to bits and its hull sniffed at and thrust aside before the bear set off shambling swiftly along after Sam, he had but one thought—to recover his boat—and he ran round towards it.

"Sam had a good start, but the bear was the faster and the gap between them closed. By the time the first lap was nearly completed Sam in his heavy seaboots was panting. Bob was between the hummocks and the loch with his precious boat in his arms.

"Did you ever play 'pickie' at school? You run and someone chases you. If you are in danger of being caught you shout 'Save me', and another runner tries to get between you and your pursuer, and thus diverts the chase to himself, and so it goes on. Well, whether Sam had this idea in his head or not I can't say, but when he reached the hummocks he shouted 'Save me' and darted behind them. The bear for the moment lost sight of him but saw Bob standing hesitating and continued towards him.

"Now it was Bob's turn to run for his life. The *Jessie* helped him a bit. She had completed her course and was jostling and wallowing beside the edge of the ice and the bear stopped long enough to render her also a total wreck before continuing. Bob ran on, sweat on his brow and bitterness in his heart—Sam by this time was likely half-way to the ship!

"But no! When he approached the hummocks there stood Sam ready again to take his turn. He had employed the short respite to take off his jacket and now ran carrying it and shouting to draw the bear's attention to himself.

c

At the half-way distance or thereby he dropped the jacket and so gained precious time, as the bear had to stop and sniff at it and take it up and turn it this way and that. Bob was watching, and profiting by Sam's example imitated his actions when it was now his turn to run again, and his jacket too was investigated in its turn.

"So it went, on and on. The bear seemed utterly tireless, and the men though running only one lap for the bear's two were becoming very weary. Soon their fur caps, long woollen mufflers, and waistcoats had one by one been shed, and one by one had been examined by the bear and thrown aside. The sun low in the south doubtless lit up the dancing waves of ocean far away and certainly made the all-pervading snow a blaze of light, but in all its course around the world that day it surely looked upon no queerer sight—a game of 'Pickie' with life the stake! And the sun alone beheld the race or so it seemed.

"Beside the ship time passed heavily. With the food and drink rationed, it always seemed a long time between meals and this morning was no exception. When at last rations were issued for the midday meal it was noticed that the two men were missing but no one worried—they would come along by and by.

"But Geordie Brown, cabin boy, as luck would have it, also came from Yell. He had naturally been interested in the construction of the model smacks. Sam was his near neighbour at home so of course he reckoned the *Jessie* was likely to be the better boat, but he was a canny soul—all the Browns were—and thought that if he could get a peep at the actual trial runs of the boats he might have a measure of inside information and be able to lay his bets with advantage to himself.

"There was no chance of slipping away from the ship, but he unobtrusively scrambled on board, and with a telescope climbed up the slanting rigging to the crow's nest. He hoped the skipper would not notice, and anyone else who did would think the skipper had sent him. When he reached the crow's nest he found his journey so far in vain; there was nothing to be seen of the two men he looked for. Thinking it a pity to have come so far to no purpose he shinned up to the mast-head and once more scanned the scene.

"His startled shout attracted the attention of all; within seconds it seemed he was down on deck again, and then on the ice, pouring out his tale of a great bear chasing the men. He had kept his wits about him and could indicate the direction too. Half a dozen men armed with muskets ran off with all the speed they could.

"At the pool the race of death continued round and round for what seemed endless time. The bear at last became wise to the tactics of his elusive prey. There came a time when Sam dodging in his turn round the back of the hummocks found that he had not shaken off the bear which clung to his heels. Bob had manfully tried to intervene by drawing attention to himself, throwing the *Mary's* hull at the retreating back of the monster. But beyond pausing in bewilderment just for a little, it refused to be distracted from the fleeing figure in front.

"Now Sam could feel or seemed to feel its hot breath on his neck, and he had reached the stage when he no longer greatly cared. And then there was the sound of shots and shouting far away. Sam ran on mechanically, but the bear stopped and hesitated uncertainly before resuming its tireless, loping run.

"The shouting increased and there came again those frightening bangs louder now behind him. He turned round to face the danger whatever it was, while Sam continued stumbling on until he dropped at Bob's feet. Too late the bear thought of escape—he had no chance against the guns which from a safe distance shot the life out of him.

"Picking up the garments strewn round the loch and

leaving two men to skin the fallen giant, the others set out
for the ships, two on either side supporting Sam and Bob.

"When they had gone about a quarter of a mile they
halted. Sam especially seemed to be utterly exhausted.
But raising his eyes he saw Bob, supported though he was,
clutching to his breast the battered hull of the *Mary*. His
eyes swept round the others and then he shouted:

" 'Where's my boat? Did none of you blasted fools think
of taking the *Jessie*?' Nor would he budge from the spot
until one of the men went back and brought him his own
badly mauled treasure!

"A few days later the crew still on the ice were rescued
by another ship. I've no doubt the *Jessie* and *Mary* got
safely to Yell, but I never heard which of them proved the
better."

2

GOTURM'S HOLE

I

IF you are ever sufficiently fortunate (or unfortunate if you are a poor sailor) to coast along the towering cliffs that forever and forever beat back the surge of the Atlantic from the north-west corner of Unst, most northerly of the Shetland Isles, you may be all agog as you pass Tonga's grim precipice to catch a first glimpse of the lighthouse on Muckle Flugga, the ultimate rocks of the British Isles. Of course if the north tide from Bluemull Sound happens to be running in the teeth of a strong north wind you may be in a condition where you "couldn't care less". But if you can, spare a glance landward to the curving rampart of cliffs.

At its innermost part, some two hundred feet above the sea and more than half-way up you may see a little recess, black in contrast with the surrounding rock. It is still marked on the Ordnance Survey Map of Scotland, one inch to the mile, as Goturm's Hole.

And thereby hangs a tale on the fringe of History's mantle, a tale unusual enough to have survived a thousand years, with a heroine who still stands forth clearly at the head of the long line of self-willed, clear-minded toiling women who throughout the many generations have made life endurable for themselves and others in a clime which ever demands the utmost effort.

As the herring smacks of fifty years ago tacked lazily and dodged each other off Tonga with a wind just sufficient to allow them to hold their own against an adverse tide, the boy outstretched on deck, his head close to the rough jersey, smelling strongly of tar and tobacco, which covered Lowrie's broad chest, heard him remark: "Yonder is

Goturm's Hole!" And the story that followed held his attention until the Westing Holms were abeam. In those days seven hundred boats sailed out of Baltasound, sixty or seventy from Uyeasound; now alas! the sea is empty of sail and the land of men.

Thorbjorn Hrollaugsson ("Tree-foot" behind his back) dwelt in Burrafirth and on this bright April morning a somewhat soured and discontented man was he, as he reflected that time had been when he was a fairly wealthy Viking in the Sogn district of Vestland over the sea in Norway. These had been happy days with leisurely cruises in the warmer seas along the coasts far to the south where the rich but unwarlike Frisian traders in their deep-bellied lumbering trading ships came adventuring north towards the Baltic, or even an occasional quick raid nearer home along Halogaland, Namdal and More. But Harold Half-dansson (curse him, and may Hela's coldest corner be his!) had put an end to all that. Little by little, first in the north, then in the west and south, he had made himself all powerful in Norway, and in the end Thorbjorn had been on the losing side at Hafrsfjord. To men like himself it had meant the end of all things, and with many others of the Sogn folk he had made his way overseas and had settled in Shetland. Here at any rate he was free and his little domain of Burrafirth, hilly and barren though most of it was, included some good land, quite good arable as well as pasture land which the Picts had held and improved for many generations. He had taken of course as much as he required for himself and the thirty-six stout fellows who, with their families and as much of their possessions as could be carried, had accompanied him from Norway. The settlement had proved easy of accomplishment. Though there had been a little resistance it was stamped out in no long time; the pathetic ruins of the Broch where the natives had put up their last fight faced his modest hall on Stackahoull. There were great gaps in its round wall, for the stone had been found very useful for building purposes. The surviving Picts had been enthralled and now toiled more or less willingly for their masters.

And he, Thorbjorn, was their master in spite of the respect and the quiet deference they paid to old Coul their priestman. Strange fellow Coul! Living in his little beehive cell and worshipping with singing and long prayers and fasting his queer feeble God, who very apparently was not a fighter like Thor nor a ruler like Odin, but believed in loving his enemies and had once even been put to a horrible death without a struggle. Well, well, let his enemies and all weaklings believe in such a god by all means—they would be all the more easily overcome! For himself Valhalla in the end was good enough. He knew some fine stout fellows already there; plenty of fighting, plenty of food and drink, and when the far distant morning of Ragnarok at last arrived, a really grand fighting finish by the side of Thor and all good fighting men. Would he be, however, among the fighting men? Would a man maimed on earth have all his limbs whole in Valhalla? One could not be quite sure. Odin himself had lost one of his eyes, and remained one-eyed even in Valhalla.

He glanced wryly at his own crippled form. His wrists and arms were substantial and strong; but his left leg was of wood, his right not as it should be, twisted a bit, and painful at times. But for Coul he would have lost that too, crushed as he had been between ship and rocks when the first landing was hurriedly made in heavy seas in face of irritating opposition from the Picts with their slings, arrows and throwing spears. Queer fellow, Coul! Lucky for him that his men had learned from the captives that their priestman was skilled in healing! Lucky for himself too! It had been touch and go for his life for a time but Coul had, pulled him through; though one leg was gone for ever nobody could help that! And the priestman had been rewarded—he was allowed to live, in comparative freedom.

But he had had to be warned not to interfere or to presume. His task was to heal men's bodies hurt in battle, to cure them of sickness, and to do him justice he did his work well. As for talking, let him talk—to the thralls! Real men, Sogn Vikings who had fought and continued to fight against Harald, that self-styled king (curse him!) disregarded him.

From the wooden bench facing northward beside the great door as he looked out on the long firth ruffled with the fresh north wind, the waves dancing and flashing here in the sunshine, and there of a sudden black from the shadows of obscuring cloud, he suddenly cried out: "Auslag, Auslag," and his daughter, mistress of the house since her mother died ten years ago, appeared almost on the instant. Tall, blue-eyed, fair-haired, bright of complexion and with rather high prominent cheek-bones, square shouldered and deep bosomed, in the bloom of age, she was worth looking at, but Thorbjorn at that moment had no eyes for her.

Pointing with the stout staff that ever accompanied him he said:

"Isn't that the Seasnake at the far side of Leera Stack; see, coming round the point?"

She looked, and keen-eyed though she was for a little she hesitated. If it was the Seasnake, then something had happened. Anlaf her brother with the best of the able bodied men had gone a week ago on a raid to Norway and should now be returning. But this did not look like a triumphant return with sail set, streamers flying and oars dipping and flashing in perfect time. The vessel was now passing the Stack, crawling slowly and unevenly like a maimed seabird past the high cliffs of flanking Saxavord.

"Yes, it's the Seasnake. I'll run down and find out what——" Without waiting for the remonstrance she knew was coming she hurried away. Thorbjorn sat anxious and angry, anxious for his son, angry at his daughter's behaviour. No woman had any right to accompany men to the beach on their departure or to greet them at the beach on their return. The proper place for good-bye and welcome was in the home.

Before Auslag reached the shore she was joined by many a hurrying boy and thrall, while from the little steadings on either side of the voe the anxious eyes of women continued to gaze. Slowly and without a hail or cheer the little longship approached the roughly built jetty at the rocky west end of the beautiful stretch of sands that bounded the south end of the firth.

To the man waiting on the bench by Stackahoull's door it seemed a long time before Auslag returned. He scarcely recognised until they stood before him the two men who accompanied her up the brae. One was Einar, Anlaf's bosom friend, strongest wrestler and best runner in the island. He had come limping and with his head bandaged. Only later did Thorbjorn learn that his right ear had been shorn away. And Ivar, the acknowledged best of a great race of seamen, the man in whose hands every boat, provided it could float, became a living joyful thing, Ivar stood, his right arm supported in a blood-stained sling. They had sailed away with Anlaf and now stood with drooping heads before Thorbjorn.

"Where is Anlaf?"

They raised their heads, looked fixedly at him for a time, their gaze firmly holding his.

"In Valhalla," said Einar at last.

Thorbjorn, his hands clenching their grasp on each other, leaned forward.

"He died well?"

"Need you ask?"

Ivar stepped forward and with his left hand laid at Thorbjorn's feet a naked sword, flashing here and dulled there with rusty stains.

"Anlaf's sword, my sword!" muttered Thorbjorn as he gazed upon it.

"Yes," said Einar, and the pain of his wounded head made him appear to grin as he clenched his teeth, "it was sent to you by his slayer with his compliments on a brave son."

"Auslag, bring them something to drink." The men drank in silence, and bowed slightly to Auslag in thanks.

"Now," said Thorbjorn, "tell your tale and briefly."

"An ill tale is soon told," replied Einar quietly, raising his hand for a moment to his head. "We reached the coast of Norway far to the south. While we were debating whether to land at once or sail north and enter a fjord by night a ship came up from the southward heavy laden and slow. We attacked, met with far stronger resistance than we had expected and in the fight had three men killed and five badly hurt. It was past noon before we took the ship, and the best of its cargo was stowed aboard until the *Snake* was so deep in the water that Anlaf would allow no more. Darkness had fallen before we turned our prow westward, leaving to the Frisian merchants who survived, their ship much lighter than before, but their throats still safe. Yesterday we had fine sailing wind and had sped so well that towards evening we judged we might reach Burrafirth by midnight.

"All the voyage we had not seen a sail but that of the ship we took, but now out of the evening haze to the south there came into view on the backboard a large ship of war. As she neared she showed a great yellow sail on which writhed emblazoned a huge red serpent. She overhauled us fast. Down dropped her sail, thirty pairs of oars flashed out, and with but eighteen men at our oars we had no hope of escape. With a great yell they drove her alongside and two huge warriors leapt aboard upon the poop where Anlaf stood. The first stumbled and Anlaf's sword was through him and out again before his body touched the deck, but the other would have cut him down had not Ivar intervened and got what you see. Before he could raise his

axe again, Anlaf's sword was through his throat. The men
at the oars were overwhelmed by a great rush from the waist
of the enemy ship; we did what we could but the fight did
not long endure. Soon we were all down or disarmed but
Anlaf, and three men now lay dead before him. Then a
squat heavy shouldered man in a fine cloak and golden
helmet, the man who seemed their leader and had taken
no part in the fighting, shouted: 'Leave him to me' and
bounded on the poop. Short time they fought and Anlaf
fell.

"They despoiled and threw the dead overboard—the sea
wolves!—their own as well as ours; they took everything
from us they wanted, all that we had taken from the
Frisian and even some of our weapons. Their dark leader
seemed to be everywhere and to attend to everything. He
smiled and talked to us, and by his tongue he was a Dane.
He asked whether any of us cared to join forces with him
and said that he could make our fortunes. We all refused
of course. He asked the name of our leader and said he was
a good lad and would have been a comrade worth his salt.
He left us sufficient food and water for our needs and even
wished us a safe voyage home. Before he left our ship with
his wolves he turned to Ivar and handed Anlaf's sword to
him!

" 'Give Anlaf's sword to Anlaf's father with Goturm's
greeting.'

"The ships parted and we left them stowing away their
plunder in the gathering darkness. And so——" only here
by a slight break in his voice did Einar show any emotion
as he looked on the old man sitting on the bench, —"and
so we came home as you see. Of the thirty men who sailed
with Anlaf eighteen are with him now in Valhalla, and of
the others two at least soon will be." He said no more, but
glanced at Ivar who gave a short nod of assent.

Auslag had quietly moved round behind Thorbjorn's
bench. Now her eyes dropped from Einar's face to her

father's head. He too had listened with look intent, but now his eyes rested upon the sword which lay at his feet, the long beautifully fashioned hilt, affording grip for both hands, the handguard with its design of intertwining bronze snakes, the blade with its significant stains. The blood of his only son was at this moment probably still on Goturm's blade. And Anlaf was now floating somewhere—a dead thing, the prey of fishes and the seabirds. He came to himself abruptly:

"You must enter the house and rest a little. Auslag, send to Coul and have him attend to the wounded, taking everyone and everything he needs. But first bid him come here to attend to these two." And Einar at any rate needed attention for his face was chalky white and he swayed where he stood. Thorbjorn rose to his feet as Auslag replied:

"Coul was at the beach even before the Seasnake reached the jetty. You know his way; he went on board with two or three others and immediately began attending to those who needed him most. He is doing all he can."

"For Oddi and Hakon," said Ivar, "he can do little; they have fought their last fight." He was a man of few words, and you would not have guessed that Hakon was his brother for whom he would have died. "But here comes the man himself."

A little bent baldheaded man, clad in a rough grey woollen mantle girdled at the waist with a strong cord from which dangled a small crucifix fashioned of bog-oak, came up to them. He bowed to Thorbjorn, slightly motioned with his hand and said: "The peace of God be with you."

Thorbjorn suddenly seemed to become aware of him. He raised his head and frowned.

"How did you find them, Coul?"

"Many are sore hurt, two very badly, but I have done what I could. The rest is in God's hands, and He can do all things."

Turning to Ivar and Einar, he sighed: "Here are others who must be attended to."

He approached Einar and speaking in a low voice indicated that he should enter the house. Thorbjorn stooped and raised the sword in his right hand and aiding himself with his staff and with Auslag beside his right shoulder led the way. Coul made Einar and Ivar seat themselves and began to busy himself about them. But Thorbjorn's mind numbed as it had been with the terrible tidings had stirred with his movement. Coul's words had enraged him beyond control. He burst forth in a shout.

"Coul, look here, what do you see here?" He drew all eyes as he dashed the sword to the stone paved floor where it klirred and rang. He pointed to it. "There lies Anlaf's sword, and Anlaf is dead—he who was laughing and singing here a week ago. And your God can do all things, can he? Let him bring back all those that are gone, let him bring back my son; nay, let him even put his slayer in my power for one hour—no, that would be too short a time—for a day, and I'll become a Whitechrist man and all my men—afterwards!"

Coul raised his hand in warning.

"Anger not God, Thorbjorn, His ways are not as ours."

Before Thorbjorn could retort there came cringing into the hall a little dark man with shaggy hair and unkempt beard. His quick eyes darted round; barefooted he shuffled to Coul's side, and with head thrust forward looked at Auslag as though for permission to speak.

"What is it, Glam, what do you here?"

"Master," he said eagerly, addressing Thorbjorn but not daring to look directly at him, "Master, great ship go down, many men die!"

"Quiet, Glam!" said Auslag, "the *Seasnake* has not sunk, but is at the beach. Why have you left your sheep at Tonga?" The summer sheep pasture was there, a fringe of

beautiful green along the top of the sheer precipices running all the way to Hermaness.

But the Pictish thrall wriggled his shoulders as he shrank
from the reproof.

"No, no, not the Seasnake, great strange ship! Before
sun came I was at cliff top but no could see far—thick mist,
so thick no could see down to water. Suddenly great crash
and men shouting, shouting! Then mist clear, whoof!
and great ship, sail flap-flap, sticking on sunken rock near
point. Big waves turn her round the rock, but she still
sticks, falling over slowly, when sudden over she go and
down, down! Two three men swim sometime here, there,
dots just like seal heads in sea, go down, down!"

Einar had sat quietly submitting to the care of Coul,
who, with linen and a basin of water wordlessly brought by
a maid on Auslag's direction, was tending a ghastly wound
on the side of his head. Now even in the process of being
bandaged he half rose from his seat.

"Glam! Did you see her sail clearly?"

"Yes, great yellow sail go flap, flap, and red snake
wriggle like mad until water drown him!"

"Goturm's ship!" shouted Ivar and Einar together.

The silence that ensued was broken by Thorbjorn. "And
they all went down; a pity, a pity!"

"Yes, no," said Glam, venturing for an instant to glance
at his master, "they go down, down, and now only one left.
He swim and swim, and rest and swim and reach cliff—no
can grip and turn and swim along and grip, and drop off in
sea again like mouse in bucket, and try again and now get
good hold, drag him up, and begin to climb."

"No one," interjected Ivar, "has ever climbed the cliffs
at Tonga." As one of the best of cragsmen he spoke from
experience.

Einar agreed. "No man ever did or ever will."

"But he climb," interposed Glam excitedly, his dark eyes
flashing, "up and up he go, sometime almost slip, sometime

stop long time, once come down a little, try this side, that
side, then up, up! Birds scream about him, flap wings, all
beside him, he no heed. He climb one hundred, two
hundred, maybe more. Now he stop in little hole in cliff—
no can do no more, cliff too steep—no go down, no go up
any more."

"Did you see him clearly? What like was he?" asked
Einar, who felt he already knew.

"He no big fair like you. He no so big, dark like me.
Big head, great strong shoulders, big arms. Bright ring on
left arm, sunshine flash on it."

Einar now rose to his feet and motioned Coul away.
"The man is Goturm," he almost shouted. "He had a ring
of gold round his left wrist. I saw it when with both his
hands he held out Anlaf's sword to Ivar. Coul's God has
given him to you!"

"Yes," said Ivar, in a voice of awe, "it must be the man
himself."

Coul's hands twitched nervously, he grasped the little
crucifix at his side and held it before him in both his hands.

Thorbjorn stood silent for quite a time. Then as one who
had reached a decision he issued his commands.

"If Coul's God has given him to me I keep my vow. For
the present and firstly let the crew of the Seasnake go or be
carried to their homes and rest to-night. Tell Raudi
Askelsson to take the young lads and go with Glam to
Tonga. Let him shout to the sea-wolf and ask his name.
It may be he will reply. Then if Raudi is certain that the
cliff cannot be scaled from the place in which the man
lurks, let him go to Pettister, gather all the thralls and
proceed south as far as Lundawick to salve anything that
has come ashore. Auslag, go with the lads and bring me
word in haste if it is he. Then if you choose, you shall help
me carve the blood-eagle on your brother's slayer. Now
go all of you and leave me."

Without a word more, they left him and he bent his gaze

upon the sword. After a time he raised his eyes to find Coul, who alone had remained, standing by the door, looking sadly and intently at him. Angered at the steady look he shouted:

"Away, man, there should be ample work for you this day, and if you find naught else to do, make ready the robes and chrismbands—when we have settled the reckoning with Goturm, I shall keep my word and we shall become your God's men."

"Man, man!" said Coul, and he raised his hand as though warding off a blow, "would you come with bloody hands to Him who said, 'Love your enemies'."

"A bargain is a bargain and my word is given. But as to loving my enemies that makes no sense at all. If I must listen to such talk it shall be later. Away!"

Coul took his departure, and almost unaware turned southward until he reached the mill not far from the end of Loch Cliff's dark waters. Turning now westward up a narrow valley which slowly climbed between bare enclosing moorclad shoulders of hilly slope, he ascended with eyes downcast and troubled mind, following the Millburn whose source was at no great distance from the headland of Tonga itself. His heart ached with pity for all the sorrow that had befallen, for all the suffering he had seen that day, and God seemed to have receded to a remote distance. So slowly did he go that just before he reached the top of the valley, Auslag, returning from the cliff, met him face to face on the footpath beside the stream. It would not have been wonderful if he had failed to recognise her. Gone were the jaunty carriage and air with which she was wont to make light of long distances and arduous work with sheep and cattle and hay; her face spoke only of utter grief and misery.

"Is it he?"

"Yes," the girl replied, "by going round a little way where the cliff top turns we can see the cave in which he

sits. On the boys shouting he came and sat with his legs
dangling over sheer space. Raudi cried out and asked him
his name and he replied: 'Goturm am I, Goturm the Dane.'
Some boy threw a stone at him and he moved back quickly
and out of sight. Raudi and all the others say the cliff
cannot be climbed."

"So there he will sit until your father drags him out and
slays him horribly."

"He slew Anlaf."

"And it gives you pleasure to think of this man being
slain in return for your brother's death?"

"It does not, it cannot bring him back, or any of those
who have gone. But I must bring the news to my father."

Coul turned back with her. He felt as helpless as if he
were in a boat lost in the mist, and they walked on in
silence, which was broken only by the murmur of the burn,
and now and then the cry of a gull or the croak of a skua.
Presently a bare point of rocky outcrop, crowned with a
tuft of grass, thrust out into the line of the stream and
here the water gurgled over rocks that barred its course.
Auslag stopped and tears filled her eyes.

"Oh, why did your gods or mine ever make men?" The
words came with a rush.

"See that tuft of grass. There when we were children,
Anlaf and I found a lark's nest with the young ones. And
we loved them and were careful not to go too near or touch
them. Even the birds know us to be hateful deadly things.
And we were happy. Why do we have to grow up? Anlaf,
who loved the little birds, and seldom spoke an angry word
to anyone, and never one to me, Anlaf grows up and kills
men who once were little boys and it may be loved birds
too, and Anlaf is killed by Goturm, and Goturm sits waiting
to be carved to death by Thorbjorn and Einar, and to-
night in Burrafirth women sit lonely, women whose sons
and husbands and lovers will come back no more. And
somewhere else are the womenfolk of those who died in

Goturm's ship, not knowing yet their loss. If the gods had to create man, why oh, why, did they make women, to toil, to grieve, weakly to try to quell the savage angers of men, to submit to men as slaves or as passing playthings, to bear children in pain and to rear them in sorrow, knowing that the little things that suck their breasts will some day mangle their fellow men and be mangled by them. Man surely was made by Loki the wicked one in one of his most evil moods!"

"And yet," said Coul gently, "there was one man far mightier than any man who ever lived, stronger if He wished even than your god Thor, wiser than your Odin. He could have overthrown whole armies with His own hand, and yet he said: 'Love your enemies,' and allowed Himself to suffer a cruel death because He loved men. Surely He thought there was some good in men to love them so."

"He was a brave man truly if He did as you say. But He died to no purpose."

"No, He tried to show man by His own example that love is greater than hatred, forgiveness than revenge, and He still lives to help those who try to follow His teaching."

"I don't understand. How can He live if He died? Some day may be you will tell me more, now I must hurry to my father."

She quickened her pace impatiently, and hurried away. Coul did not attempt to keep pace with her and was soon left behind.

II

Few except the exhausted survivors of the *Seasnake* slept soundly that night. It was late when Raudi and the boys returned to Burrafirth. They had found considerable spoil from the wrecked ship, bales of cloth, casks of wine, some oars and several spars. They had high hopes that to-morrow's tides would increase their finding and they were eager to be off again with the early dawn to Woodwick and the coast to the south. For the time being they had been almost forgetful of their dead fathers or brothers or kinsfolk, and it was only when they reached their silent homes that full realisation came to them. Not so the womenfolk who had had only their thoughts or wounded men for company.

Thorbjorn got little sleep. From a struggling but not unprosperous community his following had now been reduced to a mere handful of partly disabled men. No longer would it be possible to carry out the annual spring raid on Norway or elsewhere even on the smallest scale. Years must elapse before such a thing could again be possible and in any case Anlaf was dead. Toil and meagre return for it was all that remained to the dreary end of a cripple's life. No, not quite, he must settle accounts with the pirate first! All manner of dreadful thoughts possessed him of fiendish things to be done to the slayer of his son—boiling, burning, maiming and the blood-eagle at the last. His enemy was in his power—like a fish in a net—let him remain in his hole for a time—but not too long though, lest he should escape by death. When Goturm was dead he would become Coul's God's man. A promise was a promise and it didn't matter anyway. Nothing mattered—Anlaf was dead, his only son. Yes, but he had his slayer——so round and round went the millstone of his thoughts.

Auslag in her bed tossed wearily. She was tired but sleep did not come. Anlaf's fair hair now washed to and fro in the sea, his body rent with wounds. He would come no more, neither he nor so many of the swaggering strong fierce young men who had laughingly sailed away to trim Harald Fairhair's locks, and who had died at the hands of Goturm and his robbers. These were all dead too, except the one hapless beast who sat cowering in his hole in the cliff. Hungry and weary and frightened he must be, and when her father and Einar and Ivar and the rest dragged him out what far worse agonies would he suffer! Rightly so perhaps. Anlaf was dead and must be revenged. But Anlaf had died quickly. Anlaf had never delighted in hurting anything. Being a man he had to fight of course, but he had never hurt anything that was defenceless. Perhaps this Goturm was a man just like Anlaf—who fought because he was a man. He must be a brave man surely, and he had sent back Anlaf's sword. In Valhalla he and Anlaf might even be comrades and fight side by side when Ragnarok came. But surely they would not be comrades if Goturm came all rent and mangled and said to Anlaf: "This is what your friends did to me when I was helpless—not in a fair fight." Why must men fight? To-night a score of women were lying awake crying and mourning for their lost ones. In a few years when the half-grown lads had become men something similar would happen again either to themselves, or they would inflict like suffering on some other little place. Life had no sense at all—battle, slaughter and revenge, on and on through the ages, men fighting and dying, women toiling and weeping and always hatred, hatred!

"Love is greater than hatred." Where had she heard that? Oh, yes! Coul had said something about a great warrior or one who could have been a great warrior and who hadn't fought, but had said: "Love your enemies," and allowed himself to be killed. But that didn't make sense! Men had to fight. Why? Well, one had to kill one's enemies or be killed by them. But if no one hated, there would be no enemies, and men could live in peace. That certainly would mean happiness for women, and perhaps in time for men also. Some of them could make beautiful things of wood and metal and stone, and they seemed happy when doing so. Perhaps they could all be happy some day without any fighting. But someone would need to begin, just by not hating any more, but by trying to love even

one's enemies. The great man Coul had spoken about had
perhaps tried to begin. But he died, and yet Coul said he
was alive. That was impossible, but still there was sense in
what he had said. Could she love her enemies? She could
not; she hated the man who had killed Anlaf, the man who
was now sitting trapped like a creature in a snare, who
would by and by be dragged out, and perish in agony.
Yet he must be a brave man, he had swum until he must
have been tired, and then he had climbed or nearly climbed
the bare cliff of Tonga—no one had ever done such a thing
before.

While in every house in Burrafirth, someone found repose
hard to come by, in his little cave at his airy height in
Tonga's awesome steep, Goturm now lay fast asleep. The
rocky recess in which he lay was some five feet wide and
seven or eight deep, and in height barely sufficient to allow
him to stand erect, short as he was. Not twenty hours
before he had been one of the most powerful of the sea-
kings. Oykill and Onund with other fifteen keels of his
fleet were only some hours ahead, and the place of rendez-
vous in Jala-sound about the middle of these accursed
islands not far away. He had had a fine ship splendidly
manned, so well manned that he had started late for the
place of assembly, and had been lucky in falling in with a
little Norwegian raider filled with plunder. Goturm's luck
again! And here he was, the only survivor of that fine ship,
his fingers and toes aching and torn after such a climb as no
man ever had before, perched among the seabirds and as
remote from aid as if Hela's gates had already closed upon
him. He was utterly tired and hungry and he saw no
means of escape. The splendid vision of a kingdom of his
own in fertile England which had filled his thoughts for
years had now shrunk. A shirt and the gold ring were his
only possessions. But he still had faith in himself and in his
luck. A tiny trickle of water—too little indeed to be called
a trickle, through the porous rock at the back of the cave,

had alleviated the worst pangs of thirst. What was it the old Vala had said at Aalsund when he had asked her of his future: "Goturm forgets yesterday, toils to-day, and seeks to-morrow. High will he climb, higher than any of his sires, but never high enough for Goturm." By Odin! that prophecy had already been fulfilled! He had already that day had such a climb as surely no man ever had, and yet he was not high enough! But he would climb no more, unless he must. To-morrow he would hold forth the golden ring—it might induce someone to succour him. If not, well, when night fell, he would go forth and make the attempt again. To-night it was hopeless to try with his fingers and toes in their present state. So, overcome with utter weariness, he fell asleep.

The following day the younger men were early afield to comb the western cliffs and wicks for further spoil from the wrecked ship. The Pettister thralls accompanied them and sufficient wreckage in the form of almost half the vessel was found at Woodwick to keep them intent and busy all day. The women folk went about their menial tasks; many of them with the added care of a wounded man in the house. About midday Oddi Asgrimsson died. He had been more seriously hurt than any of the others, and from the first his case had been hopeless, but when word spread that he had gone to Odin, his loss in the weakened state of the community was felt even more than it would otherwise have been.

At night the elder men and some of the *Seasnake's* crew assembled in Thorbjorn's hall. Abundance of food and drink was set upon the long bare table, on either side of which was a long wide wooden bench, while at the top sat Thorbjorn and Auslag in seats slightly higher than the rest. Two matters were discussed, the burial of Oddi which was appointed for the following day, and the fate of Goturm. The boys had reported that he had held out a gold ring when he heard them shouting at the top of the cliff. They had pelted stones at the arm until it had been withdrawn. After various ghastly forms of punishment had been suggested, Einar said impatiently:

"He is a man, enemy though he is; let him die as a man."

Thorbjorn had listened in silence to all that had been said; now he nodded.

"The right of decision is mine. On the day after Oddi's burial, two men shall be let down to the cave. Goturm shall be bound and taken up, carved into a blood-eagle at the top of the cliff and so left till he dies. Then he shall be given honourable burial, and a cairn placed upon him, not for his own sake but for our own good name."

Auslag had been silent throughout, directing by a nod or movement of her hands rather than words Gyda and the other thrall maids who attended to the wants of the guests. But the drinking to-night was tempered by the sorrow and anxiety in every heart and, their business decided, the guests departed much earlier than had been their custom of yore.

Nor had they alone decided on a course of action. Auslag too had at last made up her mind. After a restless night she had had no peace of thought throughout the day. Several of the homes which had suffered loss she had visited. Bereavement and pain everywhere, with bitter thoughts and plans of revenge as a poor solace. She had listened too to the discussion at her father's table; hateful dreadful things had been mooted and discussed. It was all so cruel and so senseless; it would not benefit anyone; it would lead to equally savage revenge some day by someone. True the man was an enemy and had slain her brother; if he were freed he would probably continue to slay until he himself was slain. That, however, did not concern her. All she knew was that if she ever meant to have peace of mind again, she must act as she had resolved and act quickly.

When her father retired to rest, Auslag was as yet busied

about the hall. The thrall maids, who slept in the loft above the barn, departed. Gyda, the head maid, who alone slept in the house, remained, and to her Auslag turned and began speaking earnestly in a low voice. Amazement and even fear showed at first in the plain stolid countenance of the maid as she listened; it had not been intelligence but rather strength and activity that had won her favour in the eyes of her mistress. After a time she nodded and added a few words.

If Goturm had slept soundly the first night of his captivity he was in other case now. During the day he had conserved his strength ever since his brief and useless attempt to procure succour by displaying the ring. A little rag torn from his shirt and stuck in a cleft at the back of the cave gradually moistened from time to time, and this he sucked and chewed. For two days now he had been without food and felt weaker. Knowing he must make his attempt to-night, he slept or tried to sleep. But when the time came he shrank. His fingers and toes at the very thought grew painful again. He resolved, although he himself recognised it as a weakness, to wait until just before dawn; then if he must die it would be in the light of day. He drowsed uneasily as darkness came.

Between waking and sleeping he heard a sound. A stone rattled near the mouth of the cave, then another and another. Soon a further sound reached his keenly listening ears—a scuffling softer sound. Something dark swayed and dangled before the entrance of the cave, sufficiently clear against the western sky for him to see too, the rope by which it hung. He moved towards the entrance. It was a bag of some sort, swaying gently at the end of a substantial rope. Lying on his breast he reached as far forward as he dared—it was inches beyond his straining finger tips— this way and that way he tried in vain. He drew back, rose to a sitting position and with arms behind him and hands gripping hard on the ground thrust forth his feet and between them gripped and drew the bag towards him. Holding the precious rope tightly in his left hand, he undid the bag from its end; then tied the rope around his body. Only then did he open the 'bag' which on examination was a coarse smock such as haymen use. Within were oaten cakes, a small portion of smoked mutton, a little skin-bottle of wine and a seagull's feather.

As he ate and drank strength flowed back to his limbs, but swifter far, like a fire, hope ran leaping through every fibre of his being. The rope was far stouter than had been needed for the food. It was strong enough to support a man, it was meant to support him; the smock indicated disguise, the feather speed and flight. He stood up after his meal, drained the wine skin and threw it away. He donned the smock and secured the rope firmly under his armpits. Scarcely had he done so when the rope was tugged gently three times. He understood this as a signal for haste and grasping the rope with one hand stepped quickly off the ledge of his cave and immediately began to feel his way upward. It was a difficult task; the light was bad, and almost at once he was using both hands and trusting fully to the unseen hands above which maintained a steady comforting pull. Ten feet above the cave was the overhang and here he had great difficulty so much that when the bulge had been overpassed he had to pause and regain his breath. But continually for his comfort and relief there was the steady strain upon the rope, and thereafter the going was easier, toe holds and finger holds became more frequent, and with one last continuous effort he was at the top and lay exhausted, retching in the sweet grass stirred by the night wind, while billows of great darkness rolled over him, through which far off came the sound of voices.

When he recovered he found two women standing over him, the one young, fair, and handsome, the other large, shapeless, swarthy, of uncertain age. In the dim light of the April night it was difficult to perceive them clearly.

They stood apparently unconcerned, the one holding on her shoulder a stout coil of rope, the other an iron stake in her hand.

"So this is Goturm!"

The voice was certainly unconcerned and even contemptuous. He rose to his feet, swaying a little with giddiness.

"Goturm thanks you whoever you are, and by all the gods of Asgard, Goturm shall reward you."

"Reward!" said, or rather hissed the younger woman, "be silent and give careful heed!"

She pointed with the iron stake. "You must hasten south at once along the cliffs, past the two little lochs you will see on your left, until you come to Woodwick, the place where the hill descends steeply to the beach. Take any little boat you can handle and row south, keep to the west of Jala, the first large island to the south; you are safer so, and you must press on beyond Jala Sound to the great island with the high hills. There you may be safe. Here if you are found to-morrow or any day you will die by the blood eagle!"

"Why, maiden, surely here you do not war with ship-wrecked men!"

"All men must war against wild beasts."

"True, but I am not a wild beast, and torture is but the revenge of the weak. I have harmed you not."

"Goturm, three days ago you met a Norwegian ship. On its poop stood a young lad who killed three of your men before you slew him. His name was Anlaf."

"Anlaf! Yes, I believe it was. But how do you know this?"

"And you sent Anlaf's sword with your compliments to his father Thorbjorn."

"I did."

"Know, Goturm, that but a moment ago, when you lay, retching, helpless as a new-born calf, Anlaf's sister, Auslag, stood over you with this iron stake, and pondered whether to crush your skull as a beetle is trodden underfoot. Know that you are on Thorbjorn's soil and that the day following the coming day has been fixed by him and his men for your doom."

"You are the boy's sister and Thorbjorn's daughter! Then why have you done this? Are your men in hiding to take me?" He sprang aside, picked up a large stone, and gazed quickly round like a hunted creature at bay.

"You need not be afraid. Why I have acted so I know not. Better perhaps for the world if I had smashed the evil life out of you. You will do as you must do, but so must I. For me there would never have been ease of mind in after time, had I left you to be taken and tormented, so for my own sake I have saved you."

"And foregone your revenge?"

"I have foregone revenge and hatred too which hurts the hater. For me you are a poor contemptible hunted wretch. I hate you not. Go as I have directed you and take this food and drink for your journey."

She raised from the ground a little bag, placed it before him and turned away. Gyda turned with her and they had gone a few yards when Goturm ran beside them.

"Maiden," he said appealingly, keeping pace, for they stopped not. "I would not ask even to touch your hand, I cannot fittingly reward you now, I cannot even understand you." He held out towards her the bracelet of gold which he had taken from his left arm. "This ring I took from the burial mound of Hygelac the Old, a great king in days gone by. Who wears it, so they say, will become a great king too. I give it to you for yourself, or for your sons."

Auslag made no reply but waved the offering away in silence.

"Then hear me yet a moment." And in his haste he ran forward and turning stopped in their path. He held aloft the ring in his right hand.

"Auslag, each man swears by what he holds most sacred and most dear, and this ring is that to me. By this ring, I, Goturm, swear by Odin and by Thor and by all the gods of Asgard, that should I ever have the power I shall reward you, Auslag, Thorbjorn's daughter, for my life-saving, and in a manner worthy of my state and worthy of you."

For a brief moment they looked at each other; then he replaced the ring on his left arm, and with an inclination of his head stepped aside. They passed on. Neither Auslag nor Gyda looked back, but Goturm watched until their forms were lost to sight in the Milldaal. Retracing his steps he picked up the bag left by Auslag, and went hastily southwards along the cliffs, past the grey shoulder of the hill, through the sheep moor, past North Water and Heimer Water and so down the steep slope into the Daal of Woodwick as the eastern sky began to redden.

III

Sixteen years have passed over Burrafirth and the world, troubled anxious times for all dwellers on the coasts of western Europe. Harald Fairhair has not had any of his locks shorn, by his enemies at any rate. It is now twelve years since his fleet landed an army not two miles away at Haroldswick at the beginning of his conquest of the islands. After the first, and to him feeble, resistance had been overcome he had methodically cleared the islands of his enemies, those petty raiders who tried to nibble at his might. Now his henchman Sigurd was Jarl over all the Nordereys, while here and there throughout all the islands, settlers, king's men and jarl's men, had come from Norway. Thorbjorn was dead, and dead too were many of his followers in resisting Harald. Among them was Einar, who had become Auslag's husband, and she was left with little Helga and Thorsten her children. Her dwelling now was a little cot on the south side of Milldaal looking down on the north end of Loch Cliff, and her domain a few acres of bitter barren ground.

Stackahoull and its wide lands with thralls and sheep and cattle had been, for the most part, gifted by Harald himself to one of his captains, and all the better portions of the land round Haroldswick and Norwick were now occupied by him and his followers. Only round the end of the long firth were to be found some few cottages with their scraps of land, still belonging to those who had come with Thorbjorn.

Goturm's disappearance had caused great wonder and fear among them. Coul had reminded Thorbjorn of his vow that he would become a Christian after he had had Goturm in his power for a day. Thorbjorn denied that the condition had been fulfilled. His death soon after caused men to think that perhaps he had died through the anger of Coul's God, and all were inclined to look indulgently on Coul, and even at times to give some heed to his teaching. But only Auslag and one or two others of all the Viking folk openly accepted his faith. Hard and bitter as her toil was she remained quiet and serene of manner and even in a measure content.

When men had been let down to take Goturm from the cave they had found no trace of him. Had he fallen into the sea? News that a little boat was missing from Woodwick made them guess nearer the truth. Further news some weeks later of a great Danish fleet in Jalasound increased the fear that some day he would return. How he had escaped no man knew and no woman told.

But time had passed, and with the war against their own kinsfolk the earlier fear was almost forgotten. Only rarely now did mothers quell their children by warning them that Goturm would catch them if they misbehaved.

And what of Goturm? From the year 875 you will get many glimpses of him in the Anglo-Saxon Chronicle, first of all in company with his friends Oykell and Onund. "And the three kings, Gothrum, Oskytel and Anwind went with a large army from Repton to Cambridge and sat down there one year." Soon he is in command of all the Danish forces in England, restless, courageous, unsatisfied, fighting with skill and cunning against the great-souled Alfred, sometimes victorious, often thwarted, so that at last "he and his men swore on the holy ring, which they never before would do to any nation, that they would speedily depart from Alfred's kingdom."

Finally in the very year in which the invasion of Harald Fairhair completely ruined the fortunes of Auslag and her father, in the same month at Wedmore far in the south of England, Goturm the Dane and Alfred, King of England, sat side by side in lofty state. The feast was spread, harps twanged and men drank deep. Great reason was for joy— the long war was over, and these two men had divided England between them. Goturm at Alfred's request had become a Christian; the king had been godfather at his baptism, so that now according to Alfred he was Athelstan, the Rock of Honour.

Goturm was the name he himself preferred or even Guthrum as the Saxons called him. What was it the old witch had said: "Goturm will climb high—but never high enough for Goturm." Well, perhaps he would stop climbing for a bit and rest; once he had climbed—— The great, the awful cliff rose before his mind's eye, the clamouring birds, the moistened rag, the girl in the dim light of the northern night, with the iron stake in her hand. His glance passed to the golden ring on his wrist.

"Drink, man," said Alfred, "the mead is good. I know not if I ever tasted better."

The Dane complied, but without comment.

"Did you ever taste a better draught?"

"Yes, king," he replied, looking at his hands and opening and closing them, "once I drank a draught finer than ever I shall drink again even in Valhalla—or in Paradise, as I now should say."

Ever eager for a story, Alfred was not satisfied until he heard the tale in all its details—the sea fight, the wreck, the cliff, the rescue and the vow.

"And have you yet rewarded this maiden of the isles?"

"No," said Goturm, "but some day I shall, as she deserves and as I can."

"Mm," said the king, and changed the subject. She must have been a great-hearted woman this Auslag, but he could wish she had been less so, and that she had left this warrior in his cave. He trusted the Danes of course; trust was a fine thing, but a trained army and a strong navy were also fine things. And Goturm thought as he looked again on the ring: "Yes, someday I shall keep my vow—to Auslag. For the rest, forget yesterday, toil to-day, and seek to-morrow."

For the next ten years he was busily engaged in establishing his new Kingdom in East Anglia, Mercia and the north. Only once had he tried to grab a portion of Alfred's dominion, only to lose a portion of his own. Now older and more prudent, he had consolidated his power and was almost content. In England, that is; in Denmark he had hopes of further gains and turned his thoughts northwards . . .

Sixteen years then had passed after his escape from Tonga when the great yellow sail with its red serpent was seen once more in Burrafirth. One May morning to the vast dismay of the northern island, a fleet of six war-vessels, led by a huge longship of forty pairs of oars, swept with a strong tide past the headland of Outer Skaw, and swiftly turned into the narrow entrance of the firth.

Ivar, he who had brought back Anlaf's sword so many years ago, was down at the end of the sands with young Thorsten, Auslag's son. They had just returned from fishing in the firth and had pulled their coble up a little way when the boy looked seaward.

"See the ships, Ivar!" He pointed and Ivar gazed at the dreadful sail in the van, just such another as he had once seen long years ago.

"Goturm!" he cried. "Run for the hill, Thorsten, tell everyone, run!"

Bewildered eyes from the cottages were gazing on the sight. Soon "Goturm" was the one word anyone could say; with one accord all hurried, men, women, and children towards the heights. It was too late to make any stand on the beach at the landing place, but a rally might be made on the hill, though such an action could only be as hopeless as the fight against Harald had been. Ivar had hurried away to don his battle gear and remove his household. Thorsten ran all the way to his mother's house.

"Mother, Goturm has come; hurry, Mother!" he shouted, panting and pointing to the shore.

"Who says so, boy?"

"Ivar, he knew the sail and its markings."

While every other person in the community who could hurry away from the beach did so, and while men were landing from the ships in small skiffs, two persons only came towards it from the landward, Auslag and her son, the latter, brave lad though he was, following some distance behind.

Before they reached the shore, a body of about two dozen splendidly equipped warriors stood in line a hundred yards or so in front of the skiffs. Their two leaders stepped forward and one of them addressed her.

"We come in peace, lady, to learn if Auslag Thorbjorn's daughter yet lives, and if so to find her."

"You have found her, I am she."

"By Thor, I doubt you not," he answered with a great laugh. "I was told that if you yet lived you would act differently from all the rest." He turned to his men and gave a loud command, and they raised their axes high in a roaring shout that held no menace.

"Auslag, Thorbjorn's daughter," he went on, "King Goturm of Engelland gave me three commands—the first to find you, and that I have done; the second to put at your disposal for a month this fleet if you will, with all its power to use against your enemies." He paused.

She glanced at Stackahoull where stood the hall that Thorbjorn her father and his men had built; from where she stood she could see the bench on which he was wont to sit; she looked out over heathclad Hermaness, and turned her eyes to the steep slopes of Saxavord; and her inner eye saw the fair lands round green Skaw and fertile Norwick bay and the wide sweep of Haroldswick's cultivated fields. All this land had been the possession of her father and his men and might again be the possession of her son. But the thought passed quicker than lightning flash.

"I have no enemies."

Again he laughed. "Truly you are different from other women—and other men! What would we poor fighters do without enemies? But so the king said it would be, and he is wise, is our Goturm. There remains yet one command to perform." He shouted an order to the men who had remained by the skiffs, and at his words they rowed quickly back to the ships.

"Now, boy," he said, turning to Thorsten, who had stood outwardly bold, but inwardly not free from fear, beside his mother, "run away to these fellows who are playing at soldiers on the hillside." He pointed to where Erik Olafsson, master of Stackahoull was drawing up his men with the slope behind them. "Tell their leader that it is peace, that Sweyn Ormsson, King Goturm's man, would have speech with him and all his men. Go with the boy, Rollo, as proof of good faith." Rollo grinned and slightly raised his arm in acknowledgement of the order.

"Are they all to come?"

"Yes, as many as will."

At his word they departed on their errand. The soldiers

E

were permitted to relax and sat down in their ranks jesting and idly watching, some the skiffs returning laden to the beach, others the progress of Rollo and Thorsten. From the hillside they saw, after a brief pause, the body of men slowly descend, keeping good formation the while, and on the beach meanwhile two growing heaps of bales, chests and casks, of armour and apparel of every kind, as the skiffs plied between the ships and the shore.

Sweyn turned to Auslag when the advancing men halted a short distance away.

"Are you sure they are your friends?"

"They are my friends."

He stepped forward between the parties.

"Hear me, islanders, King Goturm of Engelland sent me here to find Auslag, Thorbjorn's daughter, and I have found her. He sent me to aid her if need be against her enemies." There was a sudden movement and tenseness among the men facing him.

"She tells me she has no enemies." The men relaxed. "And he has sent these gifts to her in token of his lasting friendship, and in repayment of a debt he owes." He pointed to the larger heap. "These other gifts," and he pointed to the smaller, "are for her friends. I would speak with your leader."

Erik came forward and the two men exchanging names and greetings eyed each other quietly. Sweyn saw a large dour fair-haired man with blue eyes as cold and still as the winter sea round Bornholm—a resolute fighter probably, but likely to be slow of wit and foot. Erik saw a gorgeously accoutred man with quick darting dark eyes and black trimmed beard—more a soldier than a sailor—useful in command, but man to man and hand to hand—well, Erik would not fear him.

Sweyn said: "Open speech is best, Erik. My king by his gifts has made this woman rich beyond all women possibly, in the north—he bade me make sure also that she would be safe in her riches. How can I carry out his wishes? Strong is his arm and wide his reach, but even a king's arm may be slow to ward off scathe—though quick to avenge it."

"I have not heard," replied Erik placidly, "that either the Jarl of Orkney or Harald of Norway are lacking in length of arm or width of reach either. The woman has their protection."

"I was not thinking of them, but rather of the attitude of those nearer and around her."

Erik for a little seemed not to comprehend. But when he did, his cold bleak seagull eyes were ablaze. He half raised his axe in his hand and among the two bands facing each other many a man made certain of what he knew already—that his weapon was handy.

"We are not thieves, if that is what you mean. In fair fight, weapon in hand and man against man, we *take*—we do not steal, we Northmen. Auslag, Thorbjorn's daughter, may sit amid her wealth for a hundred years with doors unbarred by night and day. She knows her countrymen, if you do not."

Sweyn's quick dark eyes searched the angry suffused face. He justly prided himself on his ability to read the hearts of men. Then he laughed.

"Glad am I to hear this, Erik!" He held out his hand, which the other after a short hesitation accepted. "Come to the beach."

The two went slowly towards the lesser heap of goods and gear upon the sand. At a gesture Sweyn's men paced behind him, and the islanders also, drawn by curiosity came slowly forward. They were followed diffidently by the women and children too, who for some time had been hovering anxiously at a distance.

Sweyn raised his hand until he drew the attention of all, then cried in a voice loud enough for all to hear.

"These gifts King Goturm sends to Auslag's friends. As you are all her friends, and you, Erik, chief man over them,

I deliver them to you to distribute and to see that no one goes portionless." (To himself he thought—no need to take hostages!—these island-beardies are honest enough with each other!)

He moved to the larger heap and Erik like a man dazed moved with him. But Sweyn looked round for Auslag, and beckoned her to stand beside him. She came and with her stood Thorsten his eyes round in wonder. As she looked down on chests filled with gold coin, on raiment sparkling with jewels, on bales of fine cloth and silks, rich armour, helmets, hauberks, drinking cups of gold and silver beautifully wrought, casks containing she knew not what, it all faded for a little. She saw it not, and once more with iron stake in hand she stood in the dim light on Tonga's cliffs looking down upon a sick half-naked man with unkempt hair and pale sweat-bedewed face. It passed, and she was in their midst, and Thorsten's hand was in hers.

"All this is yours, lady," said Sweyn, "and with it take the lasting friendship, and remembrance of Goturm who has paid his debt. Your friends will help you to carry it home."

He turned round, raised his hand in salutation to the silent throng; half turned with a special salute to Auslag, then waved his men into the waiting skiffs and without more words stepped into his own boat and was rowed away.

In a moment of time it seemed, the fleet had hoisted sail, and the great dragon ships with oar and sail sped out the firth.

Numerous and willing hands assisted in the task of bearing Auslag's treasures in triumph to her home. As the procession slowly wound along the burn, past the end of the loch and up the steep bare slope, even she could not refrain from the reflection that, while she had no enemies, the number of her friends seemed of a sudden to have multiplied.

3

DOGS AND SUPERDOGS

"Well, well, maybe he is," said my grandfather in the half amused placatory manner that so well became his years and wisdom, "maybe he is. A man should aye think his own dog best, no matter what his looks are." With this none too tactful remark he puffed profoundly at his gurgling pipe and gazed into the fire.

It was a fine fire too, built high of glowing peats which, for all his ninety years, he had himself cut and cured, for although he had a son, living nearby, devoted to him, and unostentatiously trying to lighten his every burden, although he had numerous "lazy hounds" (as he termed them) of grandsons who one and all would have been delighted to cut the peats for him, he preferred doing things for himself so as to have them, as he said, properly done. And at this moment he was well content. Seated round the fire were his son Thomas, a hard working crofter with the gift of telling highly interesting stories, a grandson with the dog which had been the subject of his remark, an old neighbour Gibbie who had called along for just a moment, as he said, for he was setting out in the night to search for his mares, because while by daylight his sight was poor, in the night he could see like a cat. Peter Anderson, too, from Littlamires had dropped in along with a cousin from Whalsay, William Irvine by name. The fair sex was represented only by a stalwart damsel of precise quick movement and rather tart manner, who managed her grandfather and all males within her orbit with the ruthless exactitude and precision of the multiplication table. Maggie was the one human being of whom my grandfather stood in awe, an awe never acknowledged, and the one human being on whom he depended, and this so obviously that he was never himself when she was out of his sight.

The inevitable cup of tea had been passed round, pipes had been lit and the ball of conversation set a-rolling by my grandfather remarking that he doubted whether Mac, my dog, would be of much use with the sheep. I had declared him to be at any rate very intelligent and, in my opinion, the best dog in the world. I now proceeded to illustrate his intelligence.

"He hates the sea and the steamer, but he hates still more to be left behind when I travel. Last summer I had to make a journey to Lerwick for a few days and while I was packing my bag he hovered around propitiatingly, wagging his tail slowly and looking at me mournfully all the time. But to his dismay, I went without him. Now a few weeks later I was again packing for a like journey and again he wandered miserably around me. I went out of the room for a moment to fetch other things for the bag, and when I returned, Mac had pulled out of the bag some of the things already packed, and lay coiled up inside the bag, gazing at me, and saying as plainly as if he had spoken the words: 'You'll not leave me this time.' And that's a true story. You can ask So-and-so and Such-and-such who were with me at the time."

Maggie, who was washing up at the table beside the back window, sniffed very audibly, and old Gibbie spat in the fire, but my grandfather laughed.

"Man, I'm no disbelieving it. I've lived long enough to believe anything either about dogs or human beings. Nae man, I think, ever kens the deeps in his ain heart, far less what's in the heart of other folk or of dogs for that matter. And just as nae man can ever tell exactly what he would do in all possible circumstances, so nobody has ever yet discovered all that a dog knows or how he knows it.

"I mind Fullerton who farmed Fairhoull had a dog Sloppy—a fine brute he was and he lived to be a very old dog nearly fifteen—but he was now getting rather blind and deaf and the work was getting beyond him. A wide stretch of land it was they had as you know, with ever so many old abandoned crofts, with stone dykes, fences, gates, burns, and what no, all the way from Smarness to the Shore. Well, one evening Peter of Colbister came along. He had two fine sheepdogs, and Fullerton and he arranged that as the time had now come around for 'caain' the sheep, Peter would come next morning with his dogs and they would gather the sheep to the house park. Fullerton explained that as Sloppy was now old and slow they would leave him at home. They would make a beginning early in the morning as it would be nearly a whole day's job for them both with the two dogs.

"Next morning when Peter arrived with his two dogs they decided after breakfast to proceed straight over the hill to the farthest point of the sheep farm about two and a half miles away and take the sheep homewards along the shore before them. The bulk of the hill shut off their view to the south and east along the coast and when they came to the fence corner farthest from the farm they were surprised when they found not a single sheep. Turning south along they passed the empty shells of the old crofts of Brakes and Mullapund, and Lower and Upper Heogs and the rest but still never a sheep. They just couldn't understand it. Then when they were now round the corner of the hill and in sight of Fairhoull with never a sheep to be seen between them and the farm they at last halted in amazement.

" 'Where can they have gone and what on earth has happened?' said Fullerton. 'Nobody can have taken them; they can't have got out to the hill through the big dyke, and along the rest of the boundary there's only the sea.' They proceeded homewards.

"Now you remember that same big dyke runs down to the sea at Hamarsberg just about half a mile from the house, and there's a bit of ground beside the gate hidden from view by an intervening brae until you are fairly near to it. When they topped this ridge there at last they saw the reason of the mystery. In front of and close to the gate itself were all the sheep and lying between the sheep and the approaching men was old Sloppy, with his head on his forepaws watching his flock. As Fullerton stood beside him he gave a wag or two of his tail but made no attempt to rise. When his master bent over him he looked up with all his soul in his eyes and then dropped his head.

"Fullerton himself was aye a hard man to all appearance and with no time for sentiment about anything, but Peter said afterwards in telling the story that on this occasion at any rate it was not so. As he raised the dog and held him in his arms the tears trickled down his cheeks. He carried him home and made him comfortable and tried him with a saucer of milk but he just lipped it and left it, and next morning he was dead.

"Now that is also a true story, and the more I think about Sloppy the more humble I feel. He must have overheard his master and Peter discussing their plans the previous evening, and in the night sometime he had slipped away. But by what miracle of skill and endurance the old dog, rheumatic, half blind and nearly deaf, had with sore toil all through the night gathered and kept together hundreds of sheep, over dykes, through fences, gates, and over burns, from the hill and the beaches, and round the loch, over all this broken ground more than three miles long and a mile wide, so as to have them snug together at last as near home as possible in front of the big dyke down by the sea, by what miracle he did it, only He above who made dogs and men knows."

There was silence for a little. Gibbie bent forward from his chair to ignite a spill of paper for his pipe, grandfather with the tongs raised a small coal to his and puffed vigorously, Thomas his son hitched his chair a little back from the fire and agreed that Sloppy had been a fine dog, that he certainly had been.

"But speaking of Fairhoull reminds me," said he in his slow deliberate manner, interspersed with cunningly chosen hesitations and pretended gropings for the right word that would have done even Churchill credit, and interspersed too, it must be admitted, with occasional sniffs from Maggie, "it reminds me of a strange kind of dog Mr. Haldane had. You remember he farmed Fairhoull after the Fullertons. This dog of his, well, there's only one word I can think of for it—it was—birsy! It wasn't shaped even like a right dog; its head was nearly half the size of its body, and it had wee beady eyes more like a pig than an ordinary dog. His master though was very proud of Scotty; he used, you remember, to drive about in a gig and took Scotty with him wherever he went. When he entered a house he would leave the dog in charge of the gig, and be he long or short away, Scotty remained on the alert keeping everyone at a distance with his bared teeth and savage wee eyes. When he fought with other dogs, and many a time he did, his style too was his very own—one foot planted slowly and firmly before another, he never moved back a step and he never uttered a sound; just a dour hard wee devil, best left alone!

"He had no fancy tricks about him such as you see sometimes in idle men's dogs," and he glanced disparagingly at Mac, who lay outstretched with his drowsy head on my foot, "he could not spell or count. The only human touch in him, if you can apply such a term, was that he would sit up and hold out his paw to his master when the master told him. But he would do it for nobody else; and the truth is that few asked him to, for he was not a fainly animal.

"He was a one man dog all right. They say his master once crossed to Yell without taking him. It was a fine morning and Scotty from the beach watched the boat on its way. Nearly four hours later the master, his business in Yell now completed, was standing chatting to some friends on the pier before entering the little boat to return. They saw what at first they took to be an otter making for the beach below the loch nearby and Mr. Haldane cried out for a gun. Mercifully, before the gun arrived, the creature landed, shook itself and came running along the shore towards them. It was Scotty—the first and only animal— or man for that matter—to swim Bluemull Sound. Blue-mull Sound, mind you, more than a mile wide and the tide running like a burn maybe as much as eight or ten miles an hour! Yes, I notice men and even women now swim the Channel to get their pictures in the papers, and maybe some of them could swim Bluemull Sound too, but still nobody has done it yet, and Scotty did. Whether he had swum to Lingey first and rested for a bit or not, nobody could ever tell.

"In the course of time the master was taken suddenly ill, and not very long afterwards passed away as we all must do. When the funeral took place Scotty was shut away in the barn. A big funeral it was; a long road the company had to travel, eight miles or so on foot away over the hills to the kirkyard at Ballster. The dog was kept in the barn for a few days until he should forget and when he was let out he wandered about miserable and disconsolate for a time. Then he disappeared. They searched high and low for him but there was no sign or word of him for a week. And then news came from the north that there was a dog lying on the new grave. A man nearby had seen him and taking pity on him when he refused to leave the place day or night, had given him water and something to eat.

"Well, they brought him home and were very kind to him, and made much of him, but he remained an unhappy sullen dog, very aloof and lonely with very little interest in anything. Then one night about two years later a very curious thing happened—a very curious thing indeed! The dog was lying in his usual corner upon an old jacket that had belonged to the master—he would lie on nothing else. Now that he was getting old he used to lie there for long stretches at a time not taking much heed of anything. But this night he suddenly jumped up out of his sleep, and stared towards the door at something nobody but he could see—his whole body quivering and shaking. Then his tail wagged with delight, he moved forward, sat down and raised his right forepaw and held it out, his eyes fixed on something close at hand. By and by he rose to his feet turned round and lay down again.

"They thought he had just been dreaming, but next morning he disappeared, and you can make a good guess where they found him. When he had felt that his end was near (and dogs have a better sense of that than we have, that they surely do!) he had taken again the long weary eight-mile journey over the hills, and was lying with his head on his forepaws, stretched out dead on his master's grave."

"In Edinburgh," I remarked after a pause, "they have a little statue erected to Greyfriars' Bobby, a dog that year after year lay on his master's grave, and could not be induced to shelter even in winter. What kind of a dog was he? I don't know; he's represented as something like an old English sheepdog, with hair down over his eyes you know, but smaller."

"Oh well! Scotty didn't get a statue, but all the same he's buried not far from where his master lies, and that will please him just as well."

Peter Anderson laughed quietly as my uncle concluded. "That's true," said he, "maybe nearer than most folk think. I knew Magnie the gravedigger there well enough. He and I were together in the old fishing days in the Jessie Jean, and ever since we have always at a regatta time foregathered and had a crack about old times. He told me he had wanted to bury the dog beside his master but some folk were shocked and spoke about consecrated ground and what not. So he said he could easily dig a hole for him just outside the kirkyard. 'I did dig the hole, Peter,' he says to me, 'but mind you I'm not saying I put anything into it. What the eye doesn't see the heart doesn't grieve about,' says he.

"But yon story of Scotty swimming Bluemull Sound," he continued reflectively, "man, it was a wonderful feat, and I find it hard to believe. Now if it had been Robbie Sutherland's dog, I've no doubt he could have swum the sound, and then swum back again."

"What Robbie was that?" asked Grandfather. "You don't mean him that was factor for the laird's estate and lived in Ordale?"

"Yes, the very man, you'll remember him far better than I can. He was a large strong man, proud of his strength, and always willing to wrestle or lift weights with anybody. He could write his name in his usual handwriting on a door with a half hundred-weight hanging by its ring from his little finger, he could lift a man on the mouth of a shovel, and hold a wheelbarrow out at arm's length by the trams."

"Oh, yes!" said Grandfather. "He certainly was strong enough—in the body, but what about his dog?"

"He had a big powerful black retriever dog. If it wasn't following Robbie somewhere it was pretty certain to be in the water. It loved swimming and was never happy out of the water. I remember one hairst after a storm there were half a dozen planks floating about in a gio near Clugan. The affrug of the waves prevented them landing and I was lying nearby above the cliffs hoping that the ebb tide might leave at least one or two stranded, when Robbie came past with his dog. He saw the planks, tied a cord to his dog's collar and said 'Fetch them.' In twenty minutes that blasted dog had every one of them ashore—for Robbie.

"He used to declare that the dog knew every word he

said, and many that he didn't say. Well, one day, Robbie had to visit the isle of Balta to see to the property in the various booths and sheds used during the fishing season. He had his bunch of keys and went into the premises one after the other, opening and shutting them all up as he went. The dog, of course, was with him. In the afternoon he recrossed the mouth of the voe to Skotaing in his boat, and it was only after he had come ashore and had his boat pulled up, and was now on his way home that he realised on feeling for his pouch and pipe that he had lost the keys. He returned to the boat and made a thorough search of it too, but it was of no avail, the keys had gone. There was nothing for it but to return to the isle. The wind, however, had freshened and was now blowing a small gale, and night was coming on, so he went home feeling very disgusted with himself at the thought of having to return to Balta Isle next day as it was very inconvenient. When he came home his wife after a little remarked on his glumness and he told her what had happened. He had lost the keys in Balta and would have to return to find them. He remembered, too, where he had likely lost them; he had taken off his jacket going down from the last hut to the beach, and they had probably dropped from the pocket at that time.

"The wind was blowing stronger, and he did not again go outside until just before going to bed. The dog had of course gone out with him. When Robbie returned he sat smoking and toasting his toes by the fire for a little, thinking of all he had to do next day, then went off to bed. During the night, however, he was awakened by a scraping at the outer door and remembered that he had not seen the dog come in with him. He got up grumbling to himself and opened the door. The dog came in and shook a shower of water over his bare legs. He put his hand down and felt the dog's coat soaking wet. Now although the wind had been high there had been no rain and he was surprised enough to light the lamp from the still glowing embers of the fire.

There stood his dog, the water dripping a little from him, and in his mouth were the missing keys!

"Now of course that wasn't such a long swim as Scotty's across Bluemull Sound but all the same it was a wonderful feat, considering that in going he had a gale of wind to contend with as well as the waves, and on the homeward journey the keys in his mouth. And he had gone, mind you, without any orders from his master, just as if he had thought the matter out for himself."

"I believe," said I, "that dogs can think, at any rate to a limited extent. Why shouldn't they? They have far keener senses of sight, hearing, and smell, than we have, and good memories too, so it's not surprising if sometimes they can put two and two together as well as we can. I remember once coming north on the *Earl* and falling into talk with a Yell sailor. He had been away for two years and we were now entering Bastavoe on a raw cold November day. As we moved on he pointed out his home on the south side of the voe, only about six hundred yards away as the crow flies, and we saw a black dog lying on the brae to the south of the house.

" 'I do believe yon's Jim,' he said; 'he was my dog. I wonder if he'll remember me.' He whistled shrilly and the dog jumped to his feet. He whistled again and the dog looked towards the steamer and ran forward a little and stopped. But when he whistled the third time the dog started to run, not down the slope towards the steamer but away almost in the other direction towards the head of the voe. It was no great time before the steamer was at anchor. The little boat for mails and passengers came and returned again to the north side of the voe, but before it reached the beach the dog had made the three-mile journey and was there dancing about on the edge of the water and barking wildly with delight.

"That dog it seems to me had the power of putting two and two together as well as a good memory. For, of course, man has always known that dogs' memories are most retentive. The Greek poet Homer nearly three thousand years ago, in telling of the return of Ulysses to his home after twenty years' absence, makes his poor old dog the only one to recognise him. It is lying neglected and dying on a dunghill, but at the sound of his voice it raises its head and pricks up its ears. When it recognises him it gives a wag of its tail and drops its ears, but is now no longer able to approach the master Ulysses it remembers from so long ago. He, however, does not yet wish to be recognised and when he passes on into the house, the dog according to the poet died forthwith when he had seen his master now after twenty years."

"High time," said Maggie, who was knitting busily, "if he was more than twenty years old." But Grandfather said softly:

"Poor brute, poor brute! What was his name?"

"Argos."

"That's a fine name for a dog. Maggie, we'll call our next dog Argos!"

"Maybe we will," she said. Naturally kind and soft-hearted, she thinks it necessary, crablike, to develop in self-defence an outer crust of brusqueness. Turning to William, who had hitherto merely listened in silence with a friendly expression of interest, she tried to draw him into the conversation.

"Have you no dogs in Whalsay to compare with the wonder dogs of Unst and Yell, not to mention Greece?"

"Na, well," said Willie Irvine slowly, and with a lovely Whalsay drawl, "we're better acquainted with fish and boats and the sea; there's not so much room in the isle for sheep and mares and kye, you know, as there is here, but I mind my father had a story of a dog that's maybe worth the telling. For this dog at any rate seems to have had an awareness that cannot be explained merely by saying that its senses were unusually sharp. Just as yon Scotty when he held out his

paw saw something that nobody else could see, so this dog
either saw or heard something that nobody else could.

"The story is well known in Whalsay and spoken of to
this day though it happened long ago in the time of the
great gale when all the boats were lost."

"Man," interrupted Peter, "that's not so long ago as all
that. I was out in it myself with old Tom Manson, as
skipper. But by the mercy of Heaven we reached
Uyea."

"Na," said Willie firmly, brushing the interruption aside
with a sweeping movement of his left hand, "na, you're
thinking about 'eighty-one. This was the great storm of
'thirty-two, the worst that ever befell Shetland so far as
man's memory goes back.

"On a fine July day, the seventeenth it was, out of a
clear sky (na, well, that's hardly true, for they say there
was a great nor-west south-east weatherhead which is still
held as the worst weatherhead in the sky), anyway, there
came suddenly a hurricane from the nor-west with showers
of hail and snow so thick that the light was shut out all
around, so that, summer day though it was, you couldn't
see a boat's length ahead. The sixerns were all out at the
fishing, some at the far Haaf, and the little open boats had
little chance of life. So for weeks and weeks afterwards
there were many anxious hearts ashore (to say nothing of
the sad hearts of them that had lost their breadwinner and
kent that they would come back no more). There were
nearly three hundred men in all missing at first, but for
more than a month afterwards boats which had been given
up as lost and gone, came back from different airts. Many
had been picked up by the big Dutch luggers and brought,
some to Lerwick, and some even to Holland first. Three
boats had landed ten days after the storm at Fair Isle—
picked up by nobody, the men just utterly worn out with
thirst and hunger, and raw with baling and rowing. But
by the time three months had passed it was realised that

more than twenty boats and a hundred and twenty men would come back no more.

"It was a sad time for all Shetland and nowhere sadder than in the Bonny Isle. From some families as many as three or four of the men folk had been lost. But as we all know from more recent experiences, life just had to go on somehow for those who were left, and gradually the numbness caused by such a disaster began to pass away a little. Some even began to forget.

"But there was one creature at any rate that did not. In one family the blow had been deadly. Tammas Hughson was a sixern skipper and with him were his two sons, Lawrence and William, and three other men. Their boat was one of those that did not return. Now Tammas had a collie dog to which he and the boys were greatly attached. It used to follow them down to the shore when they put out to sea, and was always at the beach to greet them when they returned.

"Ever since the great gale it had been disconsolate, moping and drooping about the house. For a time it had gone down to the beach every day, where it would stand gazing out to sea, or lie above the noosts watching the boats come in. Everyone knew for whom it was waiting and everyone was very kind; but in a short time it discontinued its visits and lay about the croft, remaining aloof even from the folk at home.

"So the months dragged on and winter came, and it was Christmas Eve, January fifth, for of course it was Old Style with everybody then. Nearly six months had gone from the dreadful day, and a sad morning for Christmas Eve it was. Everyone was thinking of bygone Christmasses and of those who were no longer with them.

"Well, in the morning, contrary to what was now his wont, the dog became excited and barked wildly, and after racing to and fro in front of the house it rushed off to the beach at Sandwick. Mark you, at Sandwick, a place to which it had never gone before, as it was nowhere near the usual landing place of the fishermen. On the bare lonely shore it capered madly to and fro, barking frenziedly, sometimes even standing erect on its hind feet and always looking towards the south in the direction of Bressay and Lerwick. The wind was fresh and southerly and two lads who had been going along the shore in search of driftwood stopped for a time to watch the dog's odd behaviour. Soon they were joined by little Teenie Hughson who was devoted to her brothers' dog and was uneasy whenever he was out of sight. She had followed him from the croft because she had noted his strange wild mood and was afraid something was the matter with him. By and by there was a little group of folk on the beach all looking towards Lerwick and the Mull of Eswick with Heaven knows what thoughts in their hearts. Soon someone cried out: 'There's a boat yonder close by the Voder!' and pointed to that little speck six miles away.

"Hughson and his crew, late in the evening of the awful gale, had been picked up by a Danish ship bound for America—all but one man who was crushed and killed in getting on board. The vessel had to run before the gale for several days so that there was no chance of landing the men in Shetland and they were carried to Philadelphia. There they reported to the British Consul and it was sometime later before a passage was found for them in a homeward bound ship. When in the end they arrived in Lerwick it was Xmas Eve and a Sunday morning! As you can imagine, when it was known who they were, Lerwick could not do enough for them. Offers of help of all kind and invitations to spend Christmas in Lerwick poured upon them from all sides. But the Whalsay men had only one wish—to get home that very day! Was there no chance of getting home that day? Of course there was! A willing band of young men dragged a sixern from its winter noost, and Sunday or no Sunday, off they set, and rowed them to Sandwick, the landing place nearest to Lerwick.

·"The boat had been seen, as I said, when it was miles away; more and more people had gathered, and more and more furiously excited became the dog, even rushing into the sea and barking madly when the boat was now near. Men, too, recognising the waving figures on board, rushed regardless of their Xmas clothes into the sea to meet them. But the dog was first of them all to scramble aboard lifted by a helping hand.

"Now that story my father had from his father who was one of the two boys who were out that morning along the beach in search of driftwood. The dog, vaguely hoping for months for the return of its lost friends, knew it seems to me, that they had arrived in Lerwick that morning, though Lerwick was fourteen miles away across a wintry sea. But it all comes back to what has just been said, that no man yet knows all that's in the heart and the head of a dog."

Gibbie Jarmson had been listening as intently as any of us though you would not have thought so if you had seen him reclining in the big chair opposite my grandfather. His strange light-grey eyes that could not see so well in daylight, were more than half closed, his tousled hair was grey, his long white beard spread over his grey tweed jacket, and grey too were his moleskin trousers. He could have served a sculptor as a model of patriarch or prophet and when he spoke his voice was not unworthy of his appearance. He believed all men to be wicked, and most of them thieves; all women wicked and many of them witches. That his mistrust extended even to dogs was soon evident, for on the conclusion of Willie's tale he spat into the fire and laughed briefly.

"Na, faith," said he. "You'll not easily find out all that's in a dog's head," and he stroked his beard complacently as if he himself were to some extent responsible for their astuteness. "As for his heart, the devil can enter into it too when he thinks it worth while, and when he's no busy elsewhere. That he can, believe you me! With me the sun is ower far west for me to believe all dogs as good as you seem to think.

"I remember hearing of a dog that must have been possessed of a devil just as surely as the Gadarene swine were—in fact, he behaved in the end not unlike them. Yes, that he did," and he lit his pipe once more. We waited in expectant silence, and after gathering his thoughts together for a little he began.

"I sometimes laugh when I hear of sheepdog trials and the clever things dogs do nowadays. Not such a very long time ago there was not a 'caain' dog in the whole place— they were all 'grip' dogs. When a man went out after sheep he would point out to his dog the sheep he wanted to get hold of. The dog would separate from the others the sheep required and would run after it, gradually drawing up alongside. Then with a quick clean move of its head it would grip the off foreleg and trip the sheep over on its back as neatly as you like and stay beside it until the owner gripped it. No, the sheep was never hurt, its skin never broken. The grip dogs were truly dogs worth their place about the croft and in the hill.

"But one of the Clarks of Heogsetter brought home with him from a trip to the south what he said was a real sheepdog according to the old Border farmer he had it from. It was a queer dog and seemed to know about sheep better even than its owner. It didn't so much run after them as just manœuvre about and look at them and cower down and creep so that the animals were as frightened for it as fire in the end, and went huddled together wherever it wanted to drive them. Gradually more and more folk began to have the 'caa' dogs, though for a time there was a great difference of opinion about them and lots of bickering and animosity. But the younger men especially began to favour the 'caa' dogs and in course of time there were nearly as many of the one kind as the other.

"Well, one evening Andrew Henderson, who lived at the Brakes, had been coming over the hill from the south side of Baltasound to the Shore, and in the darkening as he passed over Sobul he came on a sheep, dead, and its throat all torn and mangled. It had clearly been worried by a dog and was not very long dead. You can imagine the stir such a thing caused. The older men immediately said it had been done by one of the new 'caa' dogs, for according to their story a 'grip' dog had never been known to do such a thing. Not that that was exactly true, but certainly sheep worrying was a very rare thing indeed. The younger men and all the owners of 'caa' dogs on the other hand, said it was just impossible that a 'caa' dog could even have touched a sheep.

"James Jamieson of Noostigirt was the man that every complaint or difference had to be brought to, as he was a kind of sheriff's officer for the district and had powers to make rules and decisions as he thought best. Three or four times in the year a police officer would come north in the trading smack and take away to Lerwick maybe as many as half a dozen folk, charged with breach of the peace, drunkenness, smuggling, stealing, and God knows what not, along with the witnesses concerned. But James was a very fair-minded man in his way, and sometimes managed to smooth out quarrels without referring them to Lerwick at all.

"Now when the matter of the worrying was brought to his notice he decreed that for a week all 'caa' dogs without exceptions should be kept at home so secured that they could not leave the place. But the week had not quite ended when another sheep was found worried near Watley. Then he ordered all 'grip' dogs should in the same way be kept under observation. It was to no purpose. Another sheep went the way of the others. James was an angry man. He declared that from now on every dog without exception must have a leather collar and be secured when not in use by a chain or adequate rope; and no dog was to be used except under his own observation.

"You can imagine the exasperation of everybody at this decree of the Medes and Persians. It was bad enough to have to provide ropes or chains *and* leather collars for their dogs, but ten times worse not to be able to go out after their own sheep without having at the same time the company of James Jamieson who was next to the sheriff himself. They had to wait their turn, too, for of course he could go only with one man at a time, and so tempers began to get shorter and shorter.

"But if it was hard for the crofter, it was worse for James himself; he had no rest at all, and then to crown all another sheep was found worried. Donald Isbister of Framgord has a large family, six boys and six or seven lasses, and now his wife was just on the point of bringing another into the world. Donald had set out to Coldback for the howdie, and Meegie and he were now on their way back. Passing Hellierswater in the darkening near the old croe they both saw a dog leaving the carcass of a sheep. The sheep when they came to it was dead, but still warm. It had been worried in the same way as the others.

"Meegie, pointing to the north where the dog could still be vaguely seen slinking away, cried out: 'Follow it and see where it goes.' Donald was not too willing; he was in a hurry to get home, but she insisted. 'Away you go; faith! I should know the road to your house by this time.'

"So they parted. Meegie's work must have been well done that night for only this past summer a crowd of folk who were spending a holiday in the hotel in Baltasound came to see the Muness Castle, and one of them, a Dr. Macleod from New Zealand, came along the house and yarned away in very friendly fashion. He told me his great grandmother had been called Jeannie Isbister and that she had been born in Framgord, in this very island. Now Jeannie was the youngest of that family and had with two other sisters and three brothers emigrated to New Zealand long, long ago.

"But Donald was not so successful. When he reached the

top of the rise following the dog he could just dimly see it in the distance heading for Virse and though he said that he ran as fast as his feet could carry him, when he came there, no dog was to be seen. Maybe his heart was not in the pursuit; at any rate he hurried home, though of course next day he reported to James Jamieson the worrying and the direction the dog had taken, and where he had lost sight of it.

"Well, now, here was something at last for James to work upon. He went to Colvadale and told the men they would have to take turns in watching by night in the hill, round the Vordill and Sobul and the Hill of Colvadale. He divided them into groups of two and appointed the nights, Sundays included, when they must watch. But for a month or so nothing happened and the men concerned were beginning to grumble in real earnest (they had been cursing Donald Isbister for four weeks of course!) when something did happen at last.

"Peter Johnson of the Broch and Ned Tammas of Gairden were on the watch between Colvadale and Watley one night when they both saw a dog. Crouching close to the damp hillside they ceased to breathe as it furtively crossed the slope at an angle that was bringing it ever nearer. Suddenly Ned muttered in a whisper almost the very words that were already being shouted in Peter's heart. 'God, it's your dog!' The dog must have become aware of them and it raced away. The men followed and kept it in view for a time, for the moon a few days old helped them. Past Virse and down along the north slope of the burn they saw it clearly for a time, but you know the wilderness of dykes, burns, humps and hollows there is thereabouts and they lost sight of it at last round about Middleton.

"Peter said never a word. Since his wife had died five years before he had lived alone; the family had all gone, and he had, as he said, many a time no one to speak to but Turk, his ten-year-old sheepdog.

"Ned, too, had said nothing but by common consent the two men hurried on to the Broch. The fire had burned low, but Peter blew on the ashes and with a spill of paper lit the collie lamp hanging to the left of the fireplace near his wonted chair. Then the two proceeded through the low door to the right of the fire into the barn, Peter's hand shaking a little so that the shadows danced and fled along the rafters and over the floor like witches at a Halloween foy. Turk was lying at the end of his chain and stirred himself at their entrance, gave a wag or two of his tail, yawned and stretched himself. Peter felt a rush of relief though he could scarcely believe his eyes. Ned could not in fact believe his, and he went forward and lifted the stout chain. It was fastened at one end securely to a wooden stub driven into the ground, and at the other to Turk's collar. He drew at the chain and the dog with a slight growl and a glance at his master rose to his feet. Peter went forward, felt around his neck and said triumphantly:

" 'See, his collar is all right, too, as well as his chain.' Ashamed in his heart at having even for a moment suspected him he gave him a clap or two on the side of the head and the dog turned round and lay down, stretched out and closed his eyes.

"Well, the two men smoked and talked for a little; Peter insisted on Ned having a cup of tea before leaving and the teapot thrust into the dull ashes of the fire took quite a time to warm. They could speak only about the one thing. Who owned the worrying dog? There was no other dog in Colvadale near enough to Turk in size and colouring to be considered; further along the coast the old folk at Clugan did not have a dog; and if the dog belonged to Baltasound, wasn't it queer that he had come through Colvadale instead of going straight homewards? Ned said he would have to report at any rate to Jamieson both about the sheep and the dog they had followed, and Peter agreed though with some reluctance. He knew it meant a visit at least from James,

and there were, as you all know, lots of things about croft-
ing premises that were no man's business but the owner's;
and certainly not the business of any nosey sheriff's officer.

"Sure enough, the following night, just as Peter was
thinking of going to bed, who should come in but James
Jamieson. He had had a long tiring day, what with one
thing and another, and had not been able to set out to
Colvadale until darkness had fallen. But like myself he
could travel quite well in the dark for he had night eyes,
like most of his kin. He had on his way been in every house
in Colvadale, Virse, the Westoon, Middleton, Ludhoos,
Cunisgart, Gairden; he had learned that the men who
should be on watch were away on watch, and had seen all
the dogs and examined all their fastenings, and now he
reached the last house of his journey—the Broch.

"He heard Peter's story of the pursuit of the previous
night; he had already heard Ned's version, and declared
that to-morrow he would try the south side of Baltasound
to see if anyone had a dog of the description given. 'But
I'll have a look at your dog, so as to get the right idea of
the size and colour, and I'm checking up on all the collars
and chains in any case. Where is your dog?'

" 'He's in the barn. I gave him his supper about an hour
ago.'

"Peter took the collie lamp and led the way into the barn.
The dim light shone on the outstretched chain, and attached
to it an empty collar!

"The two men stood stock still for a long time. Then
James lifted the collar; it was the end of a man's leather
belt with a strong brass buckle, and the buckle had not
been loosed. He turned it over in his hand.

" 'He has drawn his head out through it; it's the only
thing that could have happened, that is if you are sure you
fastened it round his neck!'

" 'I did fasten it.' Peter seized the collar in a shaking
hand and held it to the light. 'You'll no tell me any dog

of his size could draw his head through a loop this size, and,' as a thought struck him, 'even if by some miracle he could, how in Heaven's name could he ever get his head back through it?'

" 'But there can't be any other explanation. He must do it somehow.'

"Peter dropped the collar and seized James by the shoulder. 'Here,' he said, his eyes flashing, 'I'll tell you. Someone having evil at me and knowing you would be coming to-night has loosed him and then fixed the collar like this.'

" 'How could anyone do that without your knowing?'

" 'Easy enough, they could have entered by the byre door, or a boy could have crept in through the sheafhole,' and he pointed to the little opening in the side wall through which the night wind caused the lamp to flicker.

"But James was dubious. Whatever he thought of their will, he didn't believe anyone about had the craftiness to do such a thing. He lifted the collar and drew the tongue of the buckle a hole tighter and fastened it. 'Let's see,' he said grimly, 'if he'll manage to get *this* over his head. It will be worth while waiting to see him try it. I'm staying here until that dog comes back.'

"And so he did. Peter remained with him in the barn for a little. Then they agreed that the dog on returning might become aware of them if they remained, and refrain from entering, so they returned to the but end of the house and kept ajar the door leading into the barn. Daylight would come somewhere between three and four in the morning, and, putting out the light, for a time they sat side by side listening in the darkness; speaking very little and only in whispers. The night wore on. By and by they took turns in watching but when the grey light of dawn began to creep through the sheafhole and the barn skylight, both men stood in silence together at the partly open door.

"To eyes accustomed to the darkness for so long the light

now seemed strong though the sun was still far below the rim of the Easting bight when there was a rush through the sheafhole and Turk stood on the barn floor. He instantly thrust his nose into the collar, stretched the chain to its fullest extent, turned his head a little to one side and lay down squirming and urging himself forward sideways along the ground. The collar jammed tighter and tighter on his nose. After straining for a time he stopped, stood up, and turning round tugged and tugged. Finally with the aid of a forepaw he dragged it off again. All this time the men had watched fascinated and still. The dog sniffed at the collar, seemed to realise what was wrong, and began scraping madly at the buckle. But soon he stopped again, gazed at the collar, pricked up his ears as though listening and then threw back his head and gave vent to a howl of such utter misery that neither of the two men ever forgot it. As they moved forward he bounded through the sheafhole and was gone.

"Peter and James rushed to the door. They saw the dog race down to the beach and stand looking seawards. James said: 'Where's your gun? I'll shoot him for you.'

" 'No,' said Peter, turning and reaching for his old musket and powder horn which he kept on a low shelf above the box bed, 'nobody shall shoot *my* dog but myself.' He put in a charge of powder from the horn, rammed down a bit of wadding and dropped in a lead ball, groped in the window until he found the little box of percussion caps, then went quickly outside and down the slope followed by James.

"There's a black rock that lies just about musket range from the shore opposite the hollow rocks on the beach folk used to call Twaemennskuddie. Peter cried out: 'Turk, Turk, come here,' and the dog turned his head, but instead of coming plunged into the sea. He swam out so fast that by the time they had reached the shore he was clambering up on the rock. There he stood looking towards the shore and Peter knelt and took careful aim. The dog did not

move, but Peter's hands were shaking a bit, and he lowered
the gun and rubbed the sweat from his forehead and eyebrows. 'No,' he said, 'I can't do it; it's a long shot and I
must make sure. We'll take the boat.' He rose to his feet.
"When James began to protest at the unnecessary
trouble Peter rounded on him like a savage. 'Damn it, he's
my dog, isn't he?' The men walked the short distance to
the boat; Peter put in the plug and began pulling away the
shords. The dog had watched them all the way, but when
they began to run the boat down the beach he plunged into
the sea again and began swimming strongly out in the
direction of the rays of the coming sun. It was a glorious
morning; the sea lay in a flat calm with light rowars
(woolly wisps) of cloud hanging high round the end of
Balta and Huney and to the south on Muness Ness. Not a
ripple was to be seen on the surface anywhere except the
clear cut lines made by the swimming dog; smaller and
smaller seemed the black head of him as he swam steadily
eastward.

"They pushed off the boat, turned her round, and James
in the bow stood up for a moment to get his direction.
'He's gone down!' he cried, and Peter rose and turned so
quickly that the little boat rocked under them. The ripple
cleaving the still water had ceased to move forward; a gull
swooped from nowhere over the end of it then soared away;
the sun's rim burst in a blaze above the sea; they looked for
a long, long time but nothing broke the surface. At last,
in silence, they rowed ashore, drew up the boat in its noost,
and James, looking at the wisps of mist melting into
nothing, remarked as he turned homewards: 'Well, I'll
have to be off, it's going to be a fine day for the peats.
Tell the men they needn't watch to-night.'

" 'Yes,' said Peter, and without another word turned
away, but when James had gone as far as the burn of
Colvadale he looked back and there was Peter still beside
the boat, still standing gazing out to sea."

So ended Gibbie's tale, and for a time we were all as silent as Peter in the story had been. Finally my grandfather asked: "And was that the end of the worryings?"

"Oh, yes," said Gibbie, "that it was. Peter never had another dog. He gave up keeping sheep and began keeping mares instead. But that reminds me, I'll have to be off looking for mine."

He rose, reached for his old cheesecutter cap, shrugged his coat comfortably on his shoulders, and as he opened the door to depart said: "So, good night be with you, and never tell me about dogs. They're like ourselves, some good and more bad." The door closed behind him; no one made any remark, but Mac, still apparently comfortably dozing beside my feet, emitted a very pronounced sniff.

4

TROUBLE WITH THE TROLLS

THORSTEN looked complacently down on the bright waters of the firth as they danced in the September sunlight. There was plenty to attract his gaze landward, too, on that beautiful morning—the cornfields already ripe for the hook, their yellow darkening and brightening as the wind waves moved over them; the hay stooks, here dotting the fields, and there being transferred by a throng of workers to the steading; the ponies had already performed their labour of bringing home the peats, the stacks were already built snugly beside the trim and neatly thatched houses. Beyond the firth, upwards and to the left, Saxavord's green slopes were dotted with sheep and lambs grazing above the great dark cliffs, and low to the right the mica sands uncovered by the ebb sparkled with the sheen of bright silver.

But Thorsten had no eyes at the moment for these things; his gaze rested on the blue waters where his new ship the Skarfr stirred at her moorings, lean and black and shining with her great dragonhead nodding sagely to the waters clucking and chuckling around her. Even Ivar had declared her as good a sea-boat as he had ever known, and the swiftest under either oars or sail, and Ivar with experience of ships extending over half a century should know.

For a young man of twenty-seven Thorsten was in reflective mood as he stood in front of the hall at Stackahoull. Strange how things had come about! Here Helga, his sister, and he had been born, though he himself had no childhood memories of the place as home. For he was but an infant when Harold the great King of Norway came, and his mother, widowed by the death of Einar in battle against the invaders, had been driven out. He remembered, not unhappily, the cottage above the loch and the steep slope on which he had played as a child while his mother toiled. Above all he recalled the unforgettable day when Goturm's fleet had sailed into the firth. He had been the very first or so he thought to see the great ships and to him above all men they had brought change of prospect. In a life of hopeless drudgery his mother suddenly found herself the wealthiest woman in all Shetland; and he as her son likely to be by reason of that wealth a person of great importance. What great days they had been to a boy of twelve, seeing the new house, large and comfortable, being built by the Millburn! Instead of the rough attentions of old Gyda only, there were now numerous thralls happy and eager at their work, and all at his beck and call; above all there had come the friendship of the sons of Harold's settlers, who had hitherto ignored the lonely lad, or had sneered at him as if he were little better than thrall-born; and at last there was Inga, the daughter of Erik, master of Stackahoull, the Jarl's most trusted friend in all the island. With her wealth and loveliness she would have been as far beyond him as the moon, had it not been for this great change of fortune.

Then following his betrothal had come the visit of the Jarl of the Isles, Torf Einar, seeking men to aid him in establishing his authority over the Orkneys, and Thorsten with many other young men had sailed away with Erik to help him. It had been a brief campaign for Torf Einar thrall-born though he was, had shown himself a great leader. His enemies were defeated, slaughtered, and in Einar's own words "given to the trolls". But on that expedition, Olaf, Erik's only son, had fallen in battle so here was Thorsten in Stackahoull. For after their return Erik had proposed that on his marriage Thorsten should make his abode there. Inga would now inherit all Erik's wide lands, Thorsten had proved himself a brave man, and the leadership of the whole north end of the island would in time naturally be his with wide lands and great wealth. He would, too, in this way knit closely together the people of the whole district, for too short a time had passed since Harold's conquest for the memories of victor and vanquished to be forgotten.

But his thoughts and his gaze returned to the Skarfr. There was a ship—his ship, built and fitted out by the best craftsmen in Bergen! There was no ship her equal in all the north and he had a crew to man her, men who in her could outrow and outsail anything afloat, men who on land, too, could stand up to the toughest of seawolves; they had proved their mettle against the Vikings who had troubled Torf Einar. He looked forward to the autumn raid he had planned. It would be a lengthy trip far south. Norway, the land of the Scots, and Alfred's England were all now too well protected. He would sail to the land of the Franks where Rollo and his men were winning much plunder. Soon the harvest would be in, and then he and his men and the Skarfr would have three months to scour the seas and be back in the firth by Yuletide.

Two young men came quickly up the slope from the beach and he did not at first recognise them. But the larger of the two evidently recognised him and shouted: "Ahoy, Thorsten!" It was Magnus Magnusson brother to Egil, his own brother-in-law, husband of Helga, who had greeted him.

"Welcome," he said, "you have chosen a fine day for a long journey. What's all the good news?"

"Ulf and I have come to see the new ship, Odin guide her!" laughed Magnus. "We are hoping you will find a place for us in the crew." Noticing the slightly embarrassed look on Thorsten's face he quickly went on.

"No, Thorsten, truth is that we have come on an errand to your mother. There has been a lot of sickness among us and Helga's baby has been ailing now for a week. She does not give any signs of improving and nothing will satisfy Helga but that your mother must let Coul come and attend to her. So here we are and have come along to see your ship while Coul makes ready, and to see you too."

"Come in, come in!"

But Magnus raised his hand in protest. "We have had both food and drink in abundance at Millburn. We came by boat up the loch, delivered our news and Auslag insisted on us having food. Then she let us come to you on condition we returned within the hour. So our time is short."

"Time for a drink at any rate," said Thorsten, and motioned with his hand in hospitable manner towards the door, "then I'll row you off, and you'll give me your opinion of the Skarfr."

An hour later the men parted company on the sands. Thorsten was pleased. From dragonhead to steering oar they had declared her beautiful—the most perfectly finished longship they had ever seen. He was relieved, too, mightily relieved that Coul was going for a time at any rate away from Burrafirth. Now his greatest worry had vanished. It would have been difficult for him to perform, before sailing, the routine sacrifices and vow-swearing ceremonies, under the reproving eyes of Coul, who worshipped a God in whom few of the Northmen believed.

Many of the thralls of course followed Coul, and Auslag his mother believed too in this strange religion and had taught both Helga and him the Christian faith. But his difficulty was that he would soon be setting out with men who one and all, believed that no luck would attend a voyage which was not preceded in the proper way with offerings to their fathers' gods. It was easy to follow his mother's religion on shore but when going to sea just impossible. If one believed in loving one's enemies, why, that would be the end of all sailing for profit! Yes, he was very glad Coul had been called away—if only he would remain away for a fortnight!

G

By the time Magnus and Ulf had made their way back
to the stream, which enters the loch just below the slope on
which stood Auslag's house, she and Coul were already
waiting by the boat. On seeing them approach, the latter
stepped into it and seated himself on the forward thwart
with the obvious intention of rowing the two freeborn
youths the three mile stretch of the loch. Magnus exchanged a few words of farewell with Auslag, then turned
towards the boat and with a smile partly of kindness and
partly of derision as he looked at the bare head and grey
beard of the bent old man cried out:

"No, this time, Coul, you are the captain and Ulf and I
will do the rowing." The old man quietly rose and seated
himself in the stern, and the young men taking their places
thrust the boat off from the shore.

Auslag said: "Coul, I rely on you. Stay as long as you
think there is need of you." He nodded, and the boat under
the strenuous strokes of two strong men sped away.

Steep somewhat bare hillsides penned in the narrow still
waters as the boat slipped swiftly along. Magnus, while his
outward gaze missed little of interest, was thinking of
Thorsten's ship. If only he and Egil could see their way to
have just such another, he could certainly find the men in
Oesund to man her. Not only that, but Egil, now a family
man, might let him take charge. Ulf Thorfinsson had almost
forgotten the ship; it was no use thinking about impossi-
bilities—such a ship was not for him, and he was thinking
more about Brenda and how he could win her—that was
another nearly impossible thing!

Old Coul, bowed with the burden of seventy-five years of
life, thought of the uselessness of his long life and of how
good God had been to him. The little green isle that he
would never see again, far away on the western shores of
the land of the Gael—his boyhood with the gentle kindly
monks—the gift of healing God had given him, so that sick
folk smiled and felt better even as he stood beside them—

his own urge for travel, until at last he had come to this place, the very remotest isle at the world's end. Here he had lived for years very happily teaching and healing until, in a moment it seemed, all had crashed into ruins with the coming of the grim heathen warriors from the sea, men who had taken with a strong hand all they wanted. For years he had suffered harsh words and hard treatment from Thorbjorn, and when the conquerors had been themselves overcome, the same hard lot at the hands of Erik and his heathen men.

Then just as swiftly as misfortune had come, there had to him at any rate come very great happiness. Auslag had become a woman of great wealth, and her first act had been to purchase from Erik all the Burrafirth thralls who had belonged to her father. He looked towards the green slopes on the right to Pettister, the place of the Picts. There they lived, in a poor bit of land it is true, but still it was their own, and there they were almost free again. But another matter made his own happiness greater than that of anyone else. Auslag had become a Christian, and her children Helga and Thorsten had been reared in the faith. He sighed as he thought of Thorsten—he was afraid for him. The expedition he was planning in that new ship of his showed that by him Auslag's teaching and his was being forgotten.

His thoughts took another turn. Now he was going to the south end of the island where he had not been for forty years. Forty years! Moses was forty years old when he left Egypt, he was another forty years older when he returned, and with still another forty years added he was allowed to see the Promised Land. He checked his thoughts with a frown—God forgive him for comparing himself in any way to Moses or to any good man! He was no leader, he humbly recognised that, God was sending him to heal a little child, Helga's baby, and he knew as he looked down at his long thin white hands, that through him God would heal her; and perhaps, who knew, it might be that there was yet some work for him to do?

The boat had reached the south end of the loch. There an attendant thrall with three roughly saddled ponies awaited them, and soon they jogged along the narrow path through the hamlet of Ballista with its autumn tinted fields on either side. On their left the long voe of Baltasound lay outstretched with never a ripple to disturb the mirror of its peaceful waters. In no long time they were ascending the bare monotonous slopes of Caldback, the thrall easily keeping pace with the sturdy ponies. Now the lands of south Unst and the islands and islets to the south lay before them, green and beautiful in a sparkling sunlit sea. Far away in a blue haze they could decry the high hills of islands yet further away. After a short breathing space for the ponies they took the long downward road and their six miles journey was soon accomplished.

In Hofudsta, Egil's home, their arrival had been anxiously awaited. In the sick room the child lay so white and still and wasted that Helga's words of welcome were spoken almost in a whisper. Egil, after entering with them, moved his great bulk to and fro about the room for a little in dumb misery, then went out into the hall and looked unseeingly out over the little loch that lay below and the quiet harbour. It seemed a long time before Coul came to his side. Egil looked the question he could not utter.

"If God wills, the child will live," said Coul.

"If it only might," muttered Egil, "we would sacrifice to Him anything in return—the half if need be of everything we possess."

And recover the child did, although the process was slow at first. At Egil's own request Coul had now remained for more than two weeks at Hofudsta and with no reluctance, for he found much work to do. Illness was widespread among the people and from morning until dusk every day he had been busy in one district or another. Westing and

Easting, Moula and Muness, and above all in Oesund itself.
Everywhere he came he brought hope and healing to free-
man and thrall alike.

The weather continued fine, the sick began rapidly to
regain strength and the work of the harvest now moved
happily forward. All hearts were thankful to Coul, and all
men sang his praises.

Auslag came on a visit to Egil and Helga, and no
one was more pleased than she to hear of Coul's good
work.

"Can you not leave him here for the winter?" queried
Egil as they sat at supper with a few guests. "In the short
time he has been with us he has put new life into us all.
There is nothing he cannot do. I believe he could help us
even against the trolls themselves."

Auslag laughed. "Do they still trouble you overmuch?
Now for many years they have let us almost alone, except
round Saxavord and Skaw in the winter time."

But Egil did not laugh with her, nor did Helga who
turned and said:

"It is not the same here, Mother, as with you in Burrafirth. I laughed too, when first I saw people grow anxious
as the dark nights lengthened. But I knew better before
the spring came. Scarcely were the hay and corn in the
yards, and the sheep gathered in the home fields when the
mischief began, and it continued throughout the winter.
Corn stacks were looted, peats stolen, sheep disappeared,
here a young calf, there a pig. Men and women became
sullen and restless, suspicion of the unknown soon became
suspicion of each other. Old enmities and animosities flared
up again, veiled hints became open accusations. No one
ventured out at night alone for fear of suspicion being
cast upon him and—the truth must be told—for fear of the
unseen. Even by moonlight people do not venture out at
night except in companies and the dark moonless nights
are dreaded. The whole land is under an evil spell, animosity

between the old settlers and the new, animosity between
neighbour and neighbour, animosity even within the four
walls of a house. When spring and the long light return
it is as if we had all passed out of a bad nightmare, though
even in summer sheep and lambs disappear in the wilder
parts of the hills in spite of constant watch. But in the
winter the trolls are the real masters of the land."

"The powers of darkness work in darkness," said Coul,
"and those whose deeds are evil shun the light. Have they
always been as troublesome?"

"Old Gunnar yonder is the man that can tell you," said
Egil, "he has been here longer than any of us. Gunnar,
old warrior, tell us the story from the beginning and how
this troll trouble began."

II

The old man so addressed was white with age, white
haired, white bearded, but his withered cheeks were ruddy,
and lively yet were the blue eyes that looked out through
their bristling fence of white eyebrows. At Egil's word he
stirred himself and bent eagerly forward. He spoke in slow
measured tones and with a vague tolerant smile at the
feebleness of latter day generations. Now and then his
words seemed to run into a rhythm that betrayed the skald
of earlier years.

"There are no men now such as there were in the days of
my youth. Odin the All-Wise has gathered them one by
one, and on Gunnar he has laid the weariest burden of all,
that for eighty years and more he should see the suns of
summer and the winter stars and die a straw-death at the
last. Higher hopes had he when the arrows sang, and the
shields clashed, and men slithered to and fro in blood on
the swaying decks, where swords and axes wove their
glittering spells, and the Valkyries swooped at Hafrsfjord.
Two brothers, Einar and Sigmund the Fair, stood by me

in the morning; good are brothers at one's back in battle, and Valhalla was theirs when the day was done.

"We who were left when the night fell withdrew in good order to our homes, leaving to Harold the victory. Hard had been the strife and pursuit there was none. We took on board our wives and children, our goods and our cattle, set fire to the homesteads, and out on the whale's path over to westward we fared to find the freedom that was no longer ours in Norway. In two days we came to this land. Six ships we had in all and ten score fighting men, and we, who had faced Hairy Harold unflinchingly, laughed in scorn when we found that here, too, we must fight. Smoke beacons rose from a dozen places in this and in the other isles. When we landed on the long sands at Sandwick we found the enemy ill-armed, but lacking neither leadership nor courage. With difficulty we made good our footing and slowly we drove them before us up the slope for half a mile. But just as we won the ridge we were attacked from left and right by thrice the numbers that had first opposed us. Here for a time we wavered and many a good man fell while the shield ring was formed. Fifteen men lie buried around Sigurd of Voss in their Viking graves near Bracknigart. But in the end the enemy fled before us and we thought the victory won.

"We buried our dead and brought our families and cattle ashore. We built shelters, and surrounded the whole with a rampart of stone. Then after some days, armed and ready for battle we explored the isle towards the north as far as the long voe. Here we met Thorbjorn's men, the lady Auslag's father, and readily agreed on a division line, for there was room for all. In our portion there were several great borgs of stone. Strong they must have been in the olden time and difficult to assail, but now some were ruinous and we had little difficulty in taking them, at Colvadale, Muness, and Oesund, for most of the defenders had died at Sandwick. Those who survived and had their homes around them either fled or gave themselves to be our servants, and here the land was very good.

"But when we went west over the land we met with further resistance, a resistance obstinately prolonged. Here we found three strong borgs well defended—separate from each other about a mile, one at the ness where the tide runs swiftly, Oganess, one above the tide voe, which we called Snarraborg, and one under Valafield to the south at Underhoull. They were all occupied and difficult to enter and had been put in repair against us. We made one attempt to take Oganess by assault but desisted after losing two or three men to no purpose, and decided to starve them out. It proved a slow business lasting several weeks. Olaf Aigrsson, who was in charge at Oganess, lost patience at last, and, with the gear we had already employed and all available masts and spars and oars, fashioned scaling ladders sufficient in number to encircle the borg around, and in the dawn attacked. He found the borg quite empty, not did any man know how the enemy had escaped. The borg was thrown down and now with Olaf's men available for service against the remaining borgs matters began to move forward and the watch was not so tedious. We made a camp near a little loch between the two towers, and dividing our force into three parts maintained the siege with two bands in their turns while the third rested in camp or brought supplies from Sandwick and the gear from Oganess. To the westward of the camp the land rose steeply, ending in the bold precipice of the Blue Mull.

"And that same Blue Mull was nearly the undoing of us all. The men encamped below it kept careless watch as being off duty and in the night were attacked by great numbers of the enemy who had crept down upon them through the heather. The men lying around Snarraborg and Underhoull hurried to their assistance seeing the signal fire, but they in turn were harassed by the defenders of the borgs who sallied out behind them, and by others who rose from the ground on either side. By dawn we were all together at the loch encampment, not without considerable loss of men, and Vigi the battleground earned its name that day. In the end, after killing many and losing several men in and around the camp, we forced them up the hill, resisting all the way, and until night there were some yet fighting behind a steep breastwork of rocks they had erected just behind the cliff top. There, too, some of our men were crippled by the great stones rolled down upon them and when we at last hewed our way over the barrier most of the survivors grappled like wildcats and died fighting, a few turned and leaped to their death from the three hundred foot precipice into the sea. That proved to be the end of all fighting for we scaled Snarraborg and Underhoull within a few days, and found only a few women, children and old folk therein.

"And so the land was settled—the survivors quietly submitted to their fate and we had peace until winter came when trouble began as the lady Helga has said. The land was infested with trolls. No one ever saw them by day— dark figures which perhaps were trolls were at rare times discerned after nightfall against the skyline on lonely skerries or barren rocks. But sheep vanished, dogs were killed, cattle died for no apparent reason, corn and produce of every kind, peats, wood, utensils of all kinds disappeared. Every man cursed the trolls and every man began to suspect his neighbour. So it continued for some years. Then, as you know, Harold the King came in war and we who were the first settlers fought against him. When that strife was over the few of us who were left became his men, and while the better lands were now given to his followers we were allowed to have as our own patches of land far from the outskirts of the township, close to dark Valafield, near the Mull or out on the headlands of Moula and Muness.

"To my lot fell a portion of land nearest to Valafield; the soil is good though we lie under the great mass of the

dark stony hill; and while the trolls annoyed everyone they
made at first our lives entirely miserable. But whether
these trolls be men or devils we do not know any more than
you. We could leave nothing outside house or barn but it
was stolen or killed. In the end we found it worth while to
set aside for them a portion of everything we had, a little
corn-stack, a little peat-stack, a few lambs outside the
houseyard, a young pig or even a young calf. Nor would
they be satisfied with little; if they were not content with
our offering they took from within the enclosure too. Some
winters such as last much more than their allotted gift was
taken. And where there is no visible person to suspect it
is so easy to suspect one's neighbour. Every winter now
old animosities and quarrels and accusations revive until
life is full of bitterness. Evil hangs over the land whether
it come from man or troll, and if Coul could heal the land
of this plague, he would be a healer indeed."

"Coul cannot but God can," the old man spoke with
confidence, "but man must play his part too. What this
land needs is a church, a place where men can assemble
and commune with their Maker, and receive clean hearts,
a place which will in time hallow the land and overcome all
the powers of evil and darkness. Egil, are you willing to
show your gratitude for God's goodness to you?"

Egil's slight hesitation was interrupted by Helga: "Of
course he is. Ask anything you will, Coul, and you shall
have it."

Coul looked at Egil who nodded.

"First of all then," he went on thoughtfully, "we shall
require a quarter of an acre of ground so situated as to be
near the centre of the district, sufficient stone and clay to
build a substantial church, a dozen men for a month to do
the building work, sufficient timber to provide a roof, doors,
window covers, benches and other fittings. I would have
liked the church to have been of hewn oak throughout and
covered with reeds," he added as some memory of his youth

flashed before him, "but the time is short and the need great."

"Timber will be your difficulty," remarked Egil, but Auslag eagerly overcame that obstacle.

"There is the wood, Egil, from Norway for the new hall you were planning. Let me buy it from you to give to Coul. You will be giving land and labour and I, too, should like to give something. I, too, am grateful for the little one's recovery."

Egil almost blushed, and stuttered that he could not dream of such a thing. Of course Coul could have the timber for nothing. Auslag, however, insisted on paying him for it as her contribution and in the end had her own way as usual.

And when she departed some days later she paused for a little on her way to speak to Coul as he supervised the work. In the clear cold autumn morning the view from the chosen knoll was pleasant. A small stretch of green turf amid the heather had been marked out with the foundation trenching. The little shallow loch above the milldam lay in front, a few gulls floating on its still waters. There was a glimpse of the bay, and Skuda Sound, and, beyond the low hills of Uyea, the soaring cliffs of Fetlar, blue in the distance; elsewhere on all sides the quiet hills. Already huge stones (some of them yet after a thousand years of exposure to rain, frost, gales and the wasting hand of Time, more than half a ton in weight) had been rolled some from half a mile away to the vicinity by the willing hands of young men, vying with each other in displays of strength. The foundation of the enclosure wall had already been partly filled and stones were in position beside it. Beside the deeper excavation which marked the position of the church itself, Coul bowed his head as she bade him come when his task was finished.

The weather continued fine and the work went on apace. There was no lack either of stone in abundance or clay of the finest from the burn nearby, and the stone masons under Coul's directions showed themselves willing and skilful. In ten days' time the church walls were six feet high, and in its solitude its grey massive bulk stood forth conspicuously against its sombre background of hill. Coul's heart sang as he saw it in the evening light from Hofudsta.

Then came a dark night of rain and storm and in the morning the walls were strewn about the ground and demolished to the foundations!

To Coul and the dismayed workmen it seemed impossible that their toil could in such a short time have been undone. Great stones had been torn from their place and thrown, rolled, or carried more than a hundred yards away in all directions, but mostly down the steepest declivity to the north towards the burn. The news spread like wildfire and soon a ring of awed spectators stood around. Coul had won all hearts, and, even supposing one or two individuals had been malicious enough to harm his work, this wanton destruction could only have been caused by a great many exerting great strength in a very short time. It was agreed that this was the greatest manifestation of troll unity in wickedness that the district had ever known.

Egil seemed to voice the general feeling. "It is no use, Coul, striving by day when the creatures of darkness have such power when the night comes. You may as well cease and save your toil."

But Coul thought otherwise. "If the work were once completed and the church consecrated not all the powers of the Devil would prevail against it. We must work by day and watch by night."

"Against human foes we could watch surely, but against those to whom darkness is light what would our watch avail? I can command the men, but I doubt if in a case like this they will obey."

Though he did not command, he put the matter before

those assembled, and on asking how many men were willing to keep watch at night until the work should be completed less than a dozen expressed their willingness, and even those, when they realised how few their numbers were, declared they would only do so if all others took their turn. When he saw the obvious reluctance of them all, Coul, as one who has made up his mind, said to Egil:

"I ask only your continued help by day. By night God, if He thinks fit, will protect His own, and I myself shall stay by the work throughout the night and do as He directs me."

Nor would he be dissuaded and when the men shame-facedly undertook to resume their building he had first of all a little shelter erected close by, and, in spite of Helga's remonstrance and even her tears, quietly took up his watch when the workers hastily departed before darkness fell. Nor was he quite alone, for Helga had insisted that at least one man every night should keep him company. Egil was not a very brave man but he had felt that as leader of the community and as a man he had no right to command others to do what he himself shrank from doing, and as the work-men departed he arrived clad in his armour, helmet, byrnie, battleaxe, sword and shield.

Coul remonstrated. "Not with these weapons, Egil, are the powers of evil to be withstood."

"Every man to his own choice and these are mine."

With night the wind which had been blowing keenly from the north died away. Outside a faint glimmer of light came from the surface of the loch to the east of them, all else faded into a vague greyness, then into darkness from an overcast sky. Close at hand, however, the glow from the peat fire burning within, shed its light through the open door of the shelter. The fire burned in an eildker, an iron basket with a long iron handle attached.

"If they come," remarked Egil, "you will carry out the fire; they hate the light, and I will be able to see what I am doing. Hausakliver (and he tapped his axe) should make an impression on some of them."

Coul shuddered. "No, let me speak to them first. I should like to go among them in the name of God to tell them what this church means, to tell them I am content to die, without raising my hand against them and without regret, if only they will allow the work to be completed in peace."

"If they come it will be with evil intent," growled the warrior, "and I shall use no words until I find that steel has no powers of persuasion. Nor shall I wait for them to strike the first blow. I shall keep watch outside close by the door. Bring the fire when I cry to you." He went out into the night.

Some time passed. A dog howled in the distance and there was a whirr of wings overhead. Both men tensed at the sound and Coul came quickly to the entrance. The sky was clearing and as the clouds swept away towards the south the stars in their countless hosts sparkled in the frosty air.

Suddenly Coul gasped and, as he grabbed Egil's arm, pointed to the south-east: "Look, look," he cried in triumph, "did I not say that God if He thought fit would protect His own." Egil looked in the direction of his outstretched arm and the two stood rigid in an awed silence. A great star blazing in brightness far beyond the brightest ever known and trailing a long streamer of golden light, hung in the sky, dimming even the bright stars of the Great Sail so that they were but faintly seen, as though veiling their lights before its majesty. All over Europe for many weeks that star was seen, frightening nearly all men with forebodings of change and war and pestilence. Here on the cold lonely hillside it filled Egil's heart with fear for the safety of his king, Harold Fairhair; a hairy golden star to him could represent but one person. But it filled Coul's trusting heart with exultation only. God had once more as in the day of creation said: "Let there be light" and there was light. He fell upon his knees.

The night passed quietly and the great star continued to flare in an untroubled sky. The workmen came immediately after sunrise and with them many more, some expecting to find the work once more overthrown, some even in the daytime half reluctant to approach. Many were convinced that Coul, warned now by heaven and earth alike, would cease from his attempt. They found him uplifted with joy, and the workmen inspired by him that day excelled themselves.

For many days in fine weather the work went on. Every evening on their departure the men looked back with pride at the building growing so visibly through the labour of their hands. The walls were almost complete and nearby lay a great heap of timber for the roof, sawn planks of pine and roughly trimmed beams of oak—Auslag's gift purchased from Egil. Night after night Coul had kept his watch in reverent awe, and in spite of his remonstrances every night someone had kept armed guard beside him. Egil had had no need to issue commands, but had chosen his companion by lot from the numerous volunteers. Nearly every night the great star had been visible, steering its blazing course among the constellations which grew dim at its approach. Higher and higher in the heavens reared its wondrous mane.

But of a sudden the fine weather broke. Rain swept over the land from the south-east, the wind increased until a violent gale raged, lashing the seas to fury and sweeping unchecked over the bleak hillside. The burns were swift-running torrents, the sodden moors a quagmire. For two days now the violence of the storm and the downpour had been almost unabated.

Nevertheless Coul was a happy man as he and Ulf Thorfinsson kept watch. Let it blow and rain, here they had a measure of shelter. He felt confident that the storm was passing and that on the following day it would be possible to begin putting on the roof. Ulf proved but a glum companion, sorry for himself that the lot had fallen on him that night for he had intended to attempt to see Brenda. Now another week might pass before such an opportunity arose again. He fidgeted and was unwilling to enter into conversation, and in spite of the wind and rain he went out, returned and went out again at brief intervals. It was past midnight before the rain began to ease. Coul thought that if the rain eased the wind might sweep the sky clear and he might see again the great star. He tended the fire and moved to the door of the hut which was turned away from the wind. The light shone out and dimly lit up the walls of the church a few yards in front. Beyond all was dark, and above not a star was to be seen. Suddenly he became aware that something was missing. Where was Ulf? "Ulf! Ulf!" he cried, but there was no reply.

As his eyes grew accustomed to the darkness he could see now the vague outline of the pile of timber to the right of the church wall. Was there not something shining dimly on the ground beside it? "Ulf!" he shouted again and ran forward.

He had found him. He lay face downwards, the back of his head a smashed and pulpy mess!

While he bent over the dead man, so stunned in mind that he had no thought of his own danger, he was seized in a strong grasp from behind, a sack of some kind was pulled over his head and drawn down over his arms, and he felt sack and arms being tightly bound to his sides. Then hands or claws seemed to raise him from the ground and he was swiftly carried away.

The journey seemed endless. For what appeared hours and hours his bearers moved along at a rapid pace. Sometimes there was a brief halt while others took their place. By his position and their movement Coul could judge when the motion changed from uphill to downhill and back again to uphill. With the wind on his right cheek he thought their course was westward, but no word was spoken, nor was there any sound of feet grating on the ground, only a faint splash at rare intervals. Their touch was clammy, cold and soft. The rain had continued sufficiently long to soak him and when it ceased he realised how cold he was and he shivered, in part perhaps at his plight, but more through the bitterly cold wind. Two thoughts filled his mind, the thought of poor Ulf so mercilessly cut short in his sins, and the thought of the church that now was certainly destroyed again. He had failed again, he had never done anything else but fail and now he was old, old indeed. "When thou art old, thou shalt stretch forth thy hands and another shall gird thee, and carry thee whither thou wouldest not." The words flashed through his mind. Truly he was being carried whither he would not and probably to some equally awful end. But immediately he writhed in contrition. God forgive him for comparing himself to the holy St. Peter, or for applying words so sacred to himself.

For a time his bearers seemed to have difficulty—the pace was very slow and evidently they were moving uphill. At last he was lowered to the ground, and then drawn forward on his back for a short distance. Of a sudden the wind had ceased and he felt he was underground. Again he was raised and carried forward slowly and with abrupt changes of direction at very short intervals. Finally he was laid down on a hard rocky surface, and the slight sound of footsteps faded away into an absolute silence.

III

By sunrise the wind had fallen to a gentle breeze and the builders, making their way from different directions to their task, quickened their wonted pace in the bracing freshness of the morning air. The sound of the little burns

H

swollen by the heavy rains was unusually loud. Now the sky was clear and there was every promise of a fine day. Before nightfall the roof should be taking shape if the weather held.

Every man as he came in sight of the church stopped and gazed, then ran forward only to slacken pace as he drew near, and to approach diffidently and slowly, waiting on his neighbour to take the lead. Where yesterday the grey walls had stood proudly in their firmness and strength, to-day there was only a confused heap of stones. Scarcely could even the outline of a building be recognised. And nearby where the timber had been piled in a neat stack was but a heap of ashes with charred ends of planks and beams in a rough ring around. Coul's little shelter too had been strewn about the ground.

As they wandered slowly and dumbly round and round, someone of keener eye saw something more than grey ashes in the centre heap, something that had a white gleam. Carefully and gently brushing aside the ashes they found all that was left of Ulf, the back of the skull crushed, whether before or after death they could not tell, the larger bones still warm to the touch.

There, too, they found the iron basket which had been used to start the blaze. But though they searched for many hours among the stones and cleared the rubble down to the very ground they found no trace of Coul. For the rest of that day and the next they searched the ground round about, then they scoured the hills and dales, even the beaches, the cliffs and the lochs, but found no trace of him. As the days lengthened to weeks and the weeks became months they realised he would not return. Coul had gone; he had been taken by the trolls.

Coul had lain for a little in the stillness, and feeling he was all alone had tentatively begun to move his cramped arms and shrug and writhe his shoulders to ease his bonds, when he found the task of his release taken from him. His bonds were loosed and the covering withdrawn. For a time he lay with his eyes closed shrinking from the sight of the devils into whose clutches he had fallen. "Though I flee to the uttermost parts of the earth, there Thou are also; if I descend into Hell, there Thou art with me." He bravely opened his eyes and looked round steadfastly.

He lay in a small cell, apparently hollowed out of rock, dimly lit by a stone lamp, filled with fish- or seal-oil, from which a lighted wick of some soft material projected. By its light he saw the two hairy figures that stood beside him. They were garbed in breeches and short cloaks of grey seal-skin, their hair matted and long, their short bristly beards unkempt, the portions of the faces visible and their hands were rough and of a bleached appearance. But it was their eyes that first gave him a little comfort; there was intelligence and interest in them.

One of them gripped his shoulder and shook him but not roughly. "Arise and come," he said in low tones but quite distinctly. In his astonishment, Coul quickly scrambled to his feet, and as the blood surged back to his long pinioned arms he swayed, his head reeled, and he felt as though he would fall. It was not the harsh language of the Viking conquerors that had been used, the tongue to which he had become inured, but the softer Pictish tongue of his boyhood and early manhood long ago. The pain of his returning circulation revived him, and he went forward with them through a low narrow tunnel of stone, so narrow that one of them preceded him while the other followed.

He entered a large and lofty cave so lofty that the light of a brightly burning peat fire scarcely penetrated to its roof. Additional light was shed from several hollowed stone lamps like that already mentioned. But Coul's attention was arrested by the cave's inmates. More than a score of people, men, women and children sat around the blazing fire, others moved about in the immediate vicinity. He was led forward to where an aged and bowed form seated on a fur-covered couch close beside the fire beckoned to him and called out:

"Welcome, Coul. Come and sit beside me."

In a daze he sat down in the vacant space indicated, and at a word food and drink were set before him, a portion of warm boiled mutton with coarse dark oaten bread, and first of all a cup of some potent drink, fiery in the throat and sending a glow of warmth all through his body. He was encouraged to eat, and while he did so looked ever and again at the figures before him and beside him, the women and children, palefaced and open-eyed, looking at him with awe, and shyly, almost fearfully, avoiding his eyes, the men very few in number and nearly all greyhaired, though none seemed to have attained to the years of the ancient being who sat crouched beside him and was looking at him, almost it seemed with affection.

One and all were clothed in sewn skins of a great variety, sometimes the variety noticeable even on a single person, skins which Coul could distinguish as of otter, seal, calf, sheep, lamb and rabbit. The stone floor of the cave too, had, around the fire at any rate, large numbers of dried skins with their fur or wool. But he was astonished to find himself observing and noting these things. Fear, which had held him unconsciously in its grip ever since he had bent over poor Ulf by the woodpile (it seemed a long time ago), suddenly released its hold, and righteous indignation took its place.

"Who are you who speak my tongue, and why have you brought me here?" His anger grew hot. "How dare you commit foul murder, and fouler sacrilege in raising your hands against the house of God? Are you really men or devils?"

The old man thrust forward his shaggy face with its eyes red and bleared with age. "Have the weary years so altered my appearance, Coul, that you do not recognise a fellow Pict? I am Elwyn, and more than forty years ago I and many others had already heard the name of Coul spoken with respect as that of a great healer. That was before the days of freedom passed for you, and life in the world above for me. Who can tell for which of us the burden has been heavier, for you slavery in the bright world above, where the dogs bark and the birds sing, and for me this life in the silence and darkness of an underground world where nothing lives but man. Your name is indeed known to us, nor should my name be unknown to you."

"Elwyn!" cried Coul in amazement. "Are you that Elwyn who was Master of the Four Brochs of the south-west. It cannot be. I have seen the man himself though I did not have speech with him, but that was more than forty years ago."

"It is so. But the day is near at hand, and we must rest. You have had a weary night, though they were told to treat you gently. Know this, however, Coul, that you are now among friends and very welcome. There will be time for talk again, but now we must rest; and rest easily, we are your friends."

He beckoned to an old man who shuffled towards them, but at this moment a band of more than a dozen younger vigorous men entered one by one through the same narrow passage by which Coul had come. Their outer covering all appeared to be of very dark otter- or seal-skin, cap, short belted coat, breeches, and leg wrappings and shoes. Amid a low babel of voices from those seated round the fire, they formed a group at a short distance from Elwyn, and stood looking at him in silence. The light from the fire lit up their faces and their dark eyes sparkled.

"Well, Otti, tell your tale! How did the work go?" Old Elwyn's voice had a trace of excitement.

A strongly built, dark and fierce-eyed youth larger than any of the others stepped forward a little from the others and spoke briefly and concisely:

"We approached in the wind and rain, and observed the

guard to come out and stand by the wood heap for a time and then return to the shelter. Hoping he would do the like again I placed men behind the pile and climbed on to it myself. When he did return I felled him with my club and he never moved thereafter. The priest came out and looked around until he found him. As he stooped over him we seized him as you instructed, and I sent four men to take him to you. I see he has arrived. After we had thrown down all the building we placed the dead man on the wood pile and fired it. When the heap was well ablaze we left and here we are."

"Well done, indeed!" Elwyn waved his hand in a gesture of dismissal, and immediately the young men relaxed and moved here and there; some seated themselves by the fire while others stood talking in low tones but in lively fashion to the older men or to the women. The old man turned to Coul and said firmly: "I know you would ask more but I am tired. Wait until we both have slept. I have much to ask you also." Coul obeying a touch on his shoulder rose and followed his guide to a little cell, whose bareness was relieved by an ample supply of skins lying in a recess large enough to form a couch. His guide set down the lamp he carried on a large stone with rudely smoothed surface and so left him.

Though sleep did not come easily, it came at last, nor did he awake until the stir and bustle and the sound of low-pitched voices in the great cave indicated that another night had come. Indeed, in all the surprises he encountered during the subsequent time he spent among them nothing seemed stranger than this, the way in which the functions of day and night were so smoothly exchanged. In time, too, all his questions were answered, most of them by Elwyn, some by the other inmates, for soon he was treated by all as a friend. It was a long tale of heroic deeds in the beginning, of sorrow and hardship and endurance, and of unquench-able but dimly burning hope. The beginning of the evil days he himself knew to some extent and could nod his head in assent as Elwyn outlined it in a few words.

"Before the heathen came, what the position was here in Unst you know as well as I. We Picts had for many hundreds of years lived in security among our thralls the little folk; gone were the days when our brochs were a place of defence for us not only against the raiding heathen from the sea but against them. For ages now they had accepted our rule, and the land was at peace, for the raiders had ceased to trouble us. They were at strife in their own land, and they were finding greater and easier spoil farther south where the armies of Rome had left the land of Britain defenceless. Following on the heels of the retreating Romans our own countrymen, too, had moved south to conquer and win fortune. Fifty years ago, Coul, I myself had two brothers who fared south with many of our best warriors, to bring back booty and fortune from the land of Albion, perhaps even to find a more spacious home for us all in a kinder land. Not one of all that band ever returned. We who were left, still, as a matter of routine, maintained the wonted watch by the brochs and the beacon points, but the old forts in many cases were allowed to decay, and some were even unoccupied. Why should we fear; no enemy now troubled us from the east, and in the south were not our own kinsmen winning fortune and homes?

"Then, and it was for the last time though we knew it not, on a bright still morning in early summer the smoky pillars rolling from the brochs of the north and east made signal, and we learned that six dragon ships were heading for the land from the east.

"As in duty bound we hastened with all the men we could muster from the Four Brochs, but by the time we reached Greenbrake above the sands the heathen had landed and almost broken the resistance. One band of them was pushing on rapidly, but we, concealed behind the ridge, took them by surprise and slew many, and began to drive them before us. But other bands soon joined them, they rallied, and we could not break them.

"We withdrew in the night. The enemy busy with the eastern brochs let us alone and we had a respite of several days to make what arrangements we could. We had a hundred fighting men left; our enemies were two to one, better armed and fierce fighters. It seemed useless to attempt to hold all four brochs, and we brought over the men from Holm Broch to Underhoull and Snabroch, placing some of the women and children in the safe hiding place of the caves where we now are, in the Blue Mull.

"We made a show of defending Oganess but only to disperse their strength to give us time to make good our preparations in the other brochs, and when the time came the garrison there too slipped away by sea to the caves. Here they waited for the final struggle. Our plan was to draw the enemy on somewhere close to the two brochs, and then attack at night not only from the secret exits of the brochs but from the Mull also. On that battle we staked everything. The enemy acted as we expected; we almost took them by surprise but in the end victory was theirs. When the night fell, the dead lay thick along Blue Mull ridge; the dozen picked men who had covered the retreat of the rest through the hidden entrance were overcome at last and died on the spot or leaped from the precipice into the sea.

"That was the end of open war for there were no fighting men left in the brochs. Here in the wide caverns of the Mull were gathered all that were left still free from the hands of the enemy and we had to consider our position. Of men able to fight, free Pict and peasant alike, there were but twenty-five left, with more than sixty women and thirty young children.

"We saw how in the next few days the dead along the slopes and by the encampment were buried, the brochs of Underhoull and Snabroch were taken, and the old folk, women and children, led away wailing over the hills. At night, though there was no darkness, our scouts watched from afar the ships, fearful that they should sail away and fearful they should remain. Remain they did. The Vikings beached their dragon ships and began to build houses and to mark out the land; soon we saw that they meant to spend at least the winter here. For months we kept close in our hiding place, living on the produce of our never failing pool, which I shall show you sometime. It was when the darker nights came that we found ways to talk to the captives, and even to rescue a few of them, before they were all herded into strong places and bound in the nighttime and kept under guard. We knew then that this was no raid, such as in olden times, but that the strangers had come to remain.

"We resolved to remain free as long as we could and ordered our lives accordingly. We ventured out by night not only on the land but on the sea, and salved much that to us was of value from the brochs of the Holm and the Ness, fuel, lamps, vessels and tools of stone. For several years the Vikings remained around the south and east bays and did not build near Snabroch and Underhoull, so that thence too in time we added to our stores. Moreover, in the first winters, we carried off many of their sheep, and picked up here and there many things of value to us which our captive friends had furtively placed for us to find. The darkness became our day and the day our night. Fuel we had in abundance as the peats we had cut in spring for the use of the four brochs lay closer to us than to the Vikings, and under the cloak of the dark we brought them in and stored them, for of storage space we lack not. The work was justly shared and, in carrying out their apportioned tasks, men and women worked diligently, and forgot in so doing a little at least of their misery. And we were not without hope. Often, after midwinter, the weather was very severe, with gales and long-lasting snow, and we thought that the sea rovers would weary of the land and depart. To brighten our darkness, in addition to a plentiful supply of fuel, we had an ample supply of seal oil and oil from fish livers. So while the Vikings were exposed to the rage of gales, and the bitter cold of dark midwinter, we were undisturbed by any winds that blew, and sat dry and warm and well fed around a blazing fire.

"As always, during the time of snow we remained within the cave, finding plenty of work to do in hollowing out rooms and quarters for ourselves, store rooms for peat, corridors and rooms for drying fish, improving the passages we used, cutting here and filling there. The women passed the time curing and softening skins for clothing, spinning the wool, and weaving and fashioning coverings of all kinds. Water we had in abundance from a spring within the rocks and so there was ample food and warmth and employment for all."

Such details Elwyn gave, and much else Coul learned from others, and principally that it had been, first through the heroism of Elwyn himself, and then through his foresight and wise control, that the little community had survived the early years and still retained not only order but a measure of cheerfulness and hope. But Coul after about a week within the cave felt wretched both in mind and body, and expressed a wish to see again the light of day. Elwyn promised that at daybreak he would show him a glimpse at least of the world above, and when almost all had withdrawn from the communal fire to their own resting places he touched Coul's arm and said: "Come and see!"

He led him through a long tunnel that sloped downwards so steeply that here and there the surface was interrupted by stone steps. Of a sudden from far off came a sound such as he had not heard for some time, the sound of the sea thudding and grumbling with a singularly hollow sound upon the rocks. The tunnel turned sharply towards the right, and Elwyn said: "Stop here until your eyes become accustomed."

The morning light dazzled them, and it was only slowly that Coul took in the scene. He was looking down from a height of fifty or more feet on a vast enclosed pool surrounded on all sides by rock. It was big enough and deep enough for half a dozen dragon ships to float upon it, and in it the sea seethed and churned with a slow easy movement. The waters were exceedingly clear so that the stones and shells upon the bottom, the tufts of seaweed, the sea urchins and the fish sculling to and fro were easily visible. Light streamed down through a long almost horizontal rent in the opposite side of the great arching roof, a rent forty feet in length by three or four in width where the outer cliff had cracked and parted.

In front of them the tunnel through which they had passed came to an end and a wide flat slope of bare dark rock spread out and descended to the water's edge. Though almost steep enough to require steps the slope had none, and the two old men descended carefully, and looked into the water. "It looks as though it were lit up from beneath as well as from above," said Coul. "God is wonderful in all his works!"

"Yes," said Elwyn, "look over yonder where the light streams in," and he pointed towards the left to a very narrow low tunnel just showing above the level of the water. "From the sea that is our only entrance, so narrow that only a small skiff can come, and then only at very low water with the occupants crouching low." Then turning towards the right he indicated a considerably larger opening entirely submerged through which the light entered through the water. "The water is never low enough to leave that entrance exposed but through it the great and ever living sea surges and the fish and seals and otters come, and a man could swim if he knew of it. But the best time to see it is not in the morning light but when the sun is setting in the western sea. Then all this pool glows and is radiant with a light like liquid moonlight.

"More than a hundred years ago three boys found this place and with lights and long cords to guide their return penetrated until they came right up through the headland itself out to the light of day again. They little thought that their discovery would some day be of such service. Here, too, we can fish undisturbed by night or day, and the fish, like our water supply, have never failed us. Nor do we fear discovery through our window," and he pointed to the great rent in the cliffs. "It is not visible from above as the top part overhangs, nor from the sea as it is far above the level of a passing boat or ship."

He went on to tell how at times in summer and autumn the fish were so numerous that they could by letting down a small circular net draw burdens of coalfish and codling from the pool; indeed, Coul afterwards saw and in other ways was aware of, in various tunnels and along ledges, drying fish hanging and even lighting up the dimness with their phosphorescence.

The talk at that time was interrupted by one who came softly down the slope behind them. Otti joined them, the biggest and strongest of the young men, he who had been the leader in the destruction of the church. He had hitherto kept somewhat aloof from Coul, and indeed was the only inmate of the cavern who seemed to feel some resentment at his presence. On this occasion, however, he was of service to them helping them in the ascent. Though their soft calfskin sandals afforded grip on the stone's smooth surface, yet both Coul and Elwyn were tired and out of breath when they reached the tunnel again.

IV

In the days or rather nights that followed, Coul heard many more details of their long struggle for existence, how for them night had become day, winter their season of greatest activity, and summer a time of rest, except that in the deep dungeons of peat-moor in the adjacent hills some of the bolder spirits kept watch and seized as chance offered a straying sheep or lamb. He heard, too, of the quarrels in the early days among the men about the women-folk when it became obvious that this cave life had become permanent. Elwyn had had to assert his authority by sheer physical prowess and in the end family groups had been established and family quarters assigned; in each group a man, his recognised and acknowledged wife and their children. The unattached women and children were assigned to the family groups in such a way that each group was at first equal in numbers to each of the others. They still found it a difficult matter to rear the young, and among them the death rate was still high; in the very early years the lack of sunshine and milk had proved fatal to a great many. But yet after all these years there were twenty men, thirty women and twenty-six children, fewer it is true than when they first came to the cave, but Elwyn was confident that they had become better adapted to the life.

For one thing, with their eyes grown accustomed to the darkness, and their ears more attuned to its sounds, they had in the night time a great advantage over the heathen above ground and could with ease avoid them. They had never quite lost contact with the thralls, on whose advice little stacks of peat, and corn, and even offerings of food had now for many years been placed at a distance from the steadings for them to take. Moreover many of them were now so reconciled to cave life that they would not abandon it, even if the chance offered.

Hope that the Vikings would go away had at one time revived, when they became aware that the invaders were fighting against newcomers of their own race, but in the end still more strange warriors had settled on the land, and new steadings were made and land cultivated nearer and ever nearer to their cave.

All had agreed that every new building was a menace

that should be hampered, hindered, and if possible destroyed, and when they saw a great new house being built in the hills beyond the south settlement and at a distance from all other houses they determined to destroy it. The name of Coul had been heard on the lips of the settlers and their thralls, and the story of his great powers of healing, and Elwyn when the report reached him yearned to look on the face of the man of whom he had heard in his youth, and to hear of the world above ground. "For my heart tells me that my own time is short. It needs must be, for of all the men who faced the Vikings by the little loch so long ago, I alone am left; and though a man clings to life even when old, I would exchange the span that yet remains to me for a few moments sitting peacefully on the green grass by Snabroch's ruined wall in the sunshine hearing the laverock sing. It is not so with most of the others; they would not now live above ground even if they could, for here only they feel at home. When, after Otti and his men had destroyed the building, you began to build it once more, we were sore frightened by the great star, and waited until it could no longer see us through the clouds. Then I bade them destroy the house again, but to bring you unharmed to me."

Coul's heart was full of sadness. The destruction of his church already seemed a little thing. What could he do to help them? He did not share Elwyn's belief that they had now adapted themselves to the unnatural life they led; he saw that some of them were thin and stunted, some disfigured by a ghostly whiteness, even a scaliness of skin, and that it was not only their garb of skins that gave them an animal appearance but their movements and habits too. His power of healing and his knowledge of all simple healing herbs he employed as never before, and the young men at his request brought back from the burns and the hillside and the homesteads grasses and herbs which he carefully described and whose virtues he as carefully explained. But although he healed many and helped all, as the weeks went by he felt his own strength passing, and realised that if he did not return to upper air he would soon die. At last he told Elwyn of his longing to go.

They were seated by the fire, round which most of the cave's inmates were gathered and when he made his request there was silence. Elwyn sat crouched in thought, rubbing his beard with his left hand. Then he said that he was too old to decide such a matter, it concerned all and must be judged by all. "Will you swear not to betray any knowledge of us?" Coul said he would swear.

Elwyn cried out for silence. He told his people that a great matter had arisen. Their honoured guest Coul now wished to depart as he felt that his strength was leaving him and he wished to die in the world above ground. He would swear by the great God whose servant he was and whose star they had seen that he would in all things keep their secret nor harm them in any way. They all loved him for he alone of all men from the world above had helped them. For his part he believed him and would let him go, but the matter concerned them all and must be judged by all. Coul added that he felt his life ebbing away. He wished to return to the north to Burrafirth to die among his own folk; he would not attempt again to rebuild his church, God would do that in His own good time; he would not even have speech with the Vikings of the south nor tell anyone what he had seen.

Hereupon round the glowing fire there arose a hubbub of sound, with wailing from the women and children who did not wish him to leave them. This, however, was sternly quelled not only by Elwyn but by all the men, who shouted to them to be silent; it was for the men alone to say.

Otti opposed his release. For the first time since the cave was inhabited a stranger knew their secret or part of it. Had not Elwyn himself shown him the sea entrance? If the knowledge of it were revealed the other entrance would be

carefully sought and perhaps found. Then all their enemies
had to do was to stop both exits and that would be the end
of them all.

Had not Otti spoken it is doubtful if Coul would have
had his wish. But Otti, though the strongest and most
reckless among them, was not popular. He had for a long
time been waiting to assume the leadership, but his harsh-
ness and hasty judgment contrasted badly with old Elwyn's
fairness, and with the memory of his great prowess and wise
counsel. In the end it was agreed that Coul (after taking
solemn oaths) should be allowed to depart.

It was after midnight when Coul accompanied by Elwyn,
Otti and Uni passed up the long tunnel to where in its great
slot of solid rock a large boulder round like a millstone
closed the exit. There Coul was blindfolded (Otti had insisted on that at least) and Elwyn bade him farewell. The
stone was rolled aside and following his guide Coul slowly
crawled through the narrow hole. Though he could not see
around him, he was aware the instant he emerged, of the
glorious freshness of the night air and the immediate sense
of roominess and space, and with a guiding hand on either
side began to descend the smooth grassy slope. By and by
the bandage was removed from his eyes, but he could see
little as the night was dark.

He was very weary, and their pace was so slow that sometimes the two men carried him for short distances. Always
he thought of God's goodness to him, and prayed Him to
help the poor creatures he was leaving. For hours and
hours they travelled so it seemed, until at last with a few
muttered words they set him down and left him.

For a long time he sat, drained of all strength; even his
thoughts were numb. He may have slept.

When he opened his eyes and looked around he was
sitting on a little knoll facing the north and water gleamed
in a loch nearby. Against the northern sky faintly lit by
the coming dawn he thought he recognised the remote top

of Saxavord. He turned to the east and south; the sky had cleared and there, still dimming the others, the great star shone, though shorn of part of his mane of fire, the star that had burned so brightly when he in his pride had looked at his church a-building. Now all that was past; never more would he be able to attempt such a thing again. He sighed. God did not need his help and had punished his pride, and yet he would have liked to have helped. Now he was too old; he had come a long way in life and he was tired. And yet he had a long journey in front of him now if he meant to reach Burrafirth by nightfall; daylight was near.

His feet and legs were cold, and a numbness seemed to grip him. Nearby a little spring welled up from the ground and he smiled as his eyes rested on it. How wonderful were the works of God! He had created in a moment that bright and blazing star to wander in splendour amid the bright lights of Heaven, and he had created this little spring too. And it might be that He who could do all things took as great delight in the little spring as in the glorious star; to the eyes of the All Wise great things might not be so great, and little things of high account. He looked up and to him the star seemed to burst out into a dazzling and wonderful light. His body sagged sideways and he turned slowly over on his face.

Old Gunnar Asleifsson and his neighbour Trond were returning from the great Yule feast at Hofudsta. The sun, low in the southern sky, had already passed half his short course over the bleak hills of Yell. There was a delightful freshness in the cold brisk air from the little lochs and burns overflowing from the recent heavy rains. So far it had been a wet winter and wet too had been the Yule feast. Thorsten of Burrafirth had returned from his sea foray with great booty, including many casks of rich old wine, and he had sent to Egil and Helga a most lavish present thereof. So the drinking had been deep, and there had been much talk

of the young men having a new ship built and of going
a-viking when the next harvest was in. The two men
slackened their pace as they approached the bare hillside
beyond which their houses Gunnarster and Trondadale
stood.

Without warning they found themselves looking down
on the dead man. That he was dead they knew, face downwards though he was; the presence of death to neither was
unfamiliar. It was obvious his end was very recent. The
handsome seal-skin coat (Elwyn's parting gift) prevented
instant recognition, but when they knelt and gently turned
the body over, they looked into the calm and peaceful face
both knew so well. Coul, whom they had liked so well, had
come back from the trolls, Coul, for whom they had
searched so long, and whom they had almost forgotten in
the midwinter festivities. They rose to their feet and gazed
around—nothing disturbed the quietness of the hills. Their
eyes sought at first the grey mound of stones almost a mile
away, distinct against its moory background, the mound
which barely three months ago had been Coul's new church.
But in emotion and perplexity the eye and mind fasten
often for anchorage on the irrelevant and even the trivial,
and Gunnar, pointing with his finger, remarked: "See,
Trond, a spring here! I've never noticed that in all the
years I have passed this spot. Strange!"

"It is strange," agreed Trond, "but we have never seen
it, because it certainly was not there for us to see." They
had only a step or two to move forward, and bending down
they saw the clear water welling up so vigorously that the
water was bunched up in a tiny heap like a baby's fist.

From the spring they looked again to the serene dead
face, and back to the spring. "Maybe," said old Gunnar
hesitatingly, "the spring is Coul's gift. The trolls did not let
him give us a church and they killed Ulf; now they have
killed him, too, but were not able to hinder him giving us
this spring."

"If Coul gave it, it must needs be good," said Trond, "for he was a good man. If you will remain here, I shall go to the house and bring men to carry him in."

And now after the long lapse of more than a thousand years does aught remain? On the Ordnance Survey map of Unst YELA BRUN, "the spring of healing" is still marked; and the spring itself still pours out its stream, and by traditional custom everyone who drinks of it contributes three stones or pebbles to the little cairn beside it. The surviving legend is that long ago a priest who had tried in vain to convert the heathen natives died there, praying that since he had not been allowed to help them while he lived, he might by his death do so, and that the spring burst out of the ground soon after. But the meaning of the original name has long been forgotten.

On the same map is still to be found, too, the name of GLATNAKIRK a name given so long ago that its meaning has been lost. The surviving story attached to the ruins is that they are of a church that never was built, the powers of darkness tearing down in the night the work that had been built by day, and that finally when one who kept watch was found dead in the morning the work was abandoned. Throughout the generations it has remained GLATNAKIRK and was held in such awe and avoidance that as recently as 1900 a contractor who was building a house, on hearing that some fine building stones brought in by his carters were from Glatnakirk, refused to use them and compelled the carters to return them. The meaning of the name has been lost, but in old Icelandic there is the verb GLATA, to destroy, and the noun GLATAN, destruction. Either way "the destroyed kirk" or the "kirk of destruction" retains the story.

Facing the slope of the Blue Mull one can still see the croft of VIGGIE, though its hearthstone has long been cold and its walls in ruins, but long ago the battle (VIGI) whose memory it kept has been among the forgotten things. The VIKINGS' GRAVES can still be seen at Bracknigirt, but from them, looking east and north one sees now only the ruined walls of what once were a score of homes, and the very name now is hardly remembered by half a dozen old folk.

The great star lives on, returning now and then, perhaps as Halley's comet, perhaps as another. Of that distant year 905 the Anglo-Saxon Chronicle says: "This year a comet appeared on the thirteenth before the Kalends of November."

The great "enclosed pool" within the Blue Mull cliffs is still there, or was in 1933, still with the light of heaven entering through the great gash in the cliff, with the only entrance for a boat so narrow and low that one had to sit crouched and propel the boat forward by touching the rock on either side with the hands. The light streamed, too, through the waters of the submerged entrance to the north-west, lighting them from beneath so that one seemed to float on moonlight. The great sloping rock was there, stretching up into the darkness, and on it were the heads and backbones of three large cod, the remains of an otter's feast.

What of the poor "trolls"? Dimly we glimpse them through the centuries on their prolonged and downward road to the inevitable end. Pathetic stories are common of their attempt to milk the cows in the byre, sometimes of their hurried departure leaving antique vessels behind. We hear of their dread of the coming daylight—for day in the course of generations would to their eyes become darkness—organised action on their part would soon cease, and as individuals they would attach themselves by night to one place and labour for some tiny recompense of food, actually set aside for them, and for what more they could steal.

That they did prolong their existence tenaciously may be

guessed from the Rev. John Brand's Account of a Visit to
Orkney and Zetland in 1700. His account is generally
exact in matters he himself saw, and, even if his credulity
in other matters is considerable, there must be *some* truth
in what he says under the heading of Evil Spirits.

"Not above forty or fifty years ago (that is about 1650)
almost every Family had a Brouny or evil Spirit so called
which served them, to whom they gave a Sacrifice for his
service, as when they Churned their Milk. . . . They also had
Stacks of Corn, which they called Brounies Stacks, which
though they were not bound with straw-ropes, or any way
fenced, as other Stacks used to be, yet the greatest Storm of
Wind was not able to blow any straw off them. . . . Now I
do not hear of any such appearances the Devil makes in
these Isles."

Stories, however, of the "trows" (for in time the "trolls"
became "trows") and of "trowie" music heard emerging
from knolls and lonely nooks of the hills continued to be told
for many generations more.

As for Coul, his very name is forgotten. Not that it
matters. He meant with his whole heart to do good, and
from such a man, though he seem to fail, a spirit goes out
which outlives him. As Carlyle says: "The true past
departs not. Nothing that was worthy in the past departs
—no truth or goodness realised by man ever dies or can
die."

5

THE WRECK OF THE *HARVEST ROSE*

THE reader is warned that this tale is different. It was told by an old haaf fisherman and to understand it one has to know a little about the haaf fisherman. He had been wont to spend most of his time in summer out at sea forty miles or so from land, with five comrades in a little open undecked boat, setting and hauling mile after mile of long lines with their baited hooks trailing at intervals along the bottom. The space at his disposal in the boat was so very limited that he even had to make his movements dependent to some extent on his neighbour; his time on the other hand was (for story telling purposes) almost unlimited, for a fishing trip begun on Monday morning might last until Friday or Saturday.

Well, one could not sit for days under such conditions without talking, if it were only in self-defence, and when one began, there was generally no need to bring one's tale to a hurried conclusion. So haaf men's tales, however slender the main theme, marched on leisurely like a saga or an epic poem, introducing episodes, sometimes in themselves containing episodes, and ever returning to the main theme only to diverge again. The speaker was unhurried, his audience patient and even helpful with a few interpolated questions or comments; and as each fresh character entered the tale he had to be satisfactorily introduced before the story moved on. Their tales in fact resembled their own long lines which had to be hauled steadily to deal with the hooked fish, here a ling or cod, there perhaps a worthless dogfish, at times a large halibut. Each was dealt with in

turn while the boat swung, now to larboard now to starboard, but no matter, the hauling went on to the anchored
inevitable end where the marking buoy floated in the
distance.

The following tale illustrates, though very imperfectly,
the great gift of narration the haaf men possessed. It
suffers from my own defective memory which retains less
than half the gist of the whole tale, and only a little of the
style; from my foolish haste to get to the end of the story;
and from an interruption which led to its hurried and
premature conclusion.

I had received a piece of wood from a friend to repair a
damaged gate, and he remarked that he believed his grandfather had acquired this bit of teak long years ago when the
Harvest Rose was wrecked. When I asked about the story
of the wreck he laughed and said: "Well, I could give you
the bare outlines, but to hear that story properly told you
should get old Peter to tell it."

And so it came to pass that one day I called on old
Peter, and after we had discussed the weather as it deserved
and the weather forecasts as they deserved, we soon worked
round to the perils of the sea, and I asked him if he remembered the wreck of the *Harvest Rose*. He did, and for the
benefit of those unfortunate readers whose native language
is not Shetlandic, and of those Shetlanders who find it
easier to speak than to read the language, I have employed
English (or Scots) spelling generally, and have added a
short vocabulary of the more unusual words or expressions.

"Can I mind the wreck o' the *Harvest Rose*?" quoth he;
"as well as I mind yesterday! It was a fine fresh morning
near the end o' the hairst with a very strong sudwasterly
wind and I was shairin' corn, cutting it with the heuk of
course. There werena sae mony tractors and reaping
machines thenadays. Na, be me sang, by the time a man
had been shairing for a week his back kent aboot it. Boy,
what think you o' aa this newfangled gear that does aa the

work for everybody? What I say is peace be with the days when every croft needed five or sax strong workers to keep it going—aye, and had the workers too! Now it has an iron machine, driven with stinking oil, or gets a loan o' one, and what muckle better off they are noo I canna see! Thenadays they had their ain grice and sheep and sometimes a coo salted for the winter, and noo they have their tractors and their ration books, and, maybe if they're lucky, tippence worth mair o' this tinned beef at a Christmas time. Man, I think the whole world is clean mad noo!

"I was in alang peerie Jamie, neist door, the streen, and he oot with his package o' fagareeks, and made me take one. I rooked and pluffed at it to please him, and he puffed awa too, and I thought to myself—God teach me! When I was a boy I aye thought I was a hard smoker—two ounces of tobacco a week cost me sixpence, and here's Jamie and me puffing at this twa strae pencils, and spending nearly sixpence in ten minutes. Jamie had on a bonnie pair o' lorn shune, split new they looked and I said: 'Weel brook dee new! I ken they were a penny.'

" 'You'll never guess!' says he.

" 'Weel,' says I, sticking what was left o' the fagareek in my pipe, 'I'll warrant they'll be twenty shillings.'

"He leuch. 'I paid forty-sivin shillings for them. I aye liked good shoes ever since I could wear them.'

" 'Shall I tell dee,' says I, 'aboot my first pair? O dear, a dear! I'd been working as a beach boy for twal weeks— most o' the summer, frae the riving o' the dim till sunset, and the time came to settle up for my winnings. I'd made up my mind to get moleskin troosers and a pair o' boots so that I could go to school in winter. Counting day came and I went into the shop where Seemon Firsel was standing blinking behind the counter wi' his glasses on his broo. I think I see him yet—a peerie dry withered boddy he was. We boys called him Auld Fower-eyes, from the way he wore his glasses.'

" 'What does du want, boy?' says he.

" 'A'm come to settle up for me wages,' says I. 'A'm been beach boy for twal weeks ootbye at the pier.'

" 'O, yea, Peter, weel, weel, let's see.'

"He puts the glasses on his nose, lifts down a large ledger, opens it and runs his nose ower the pages until he came to my name.

" 'Yiss, yiss,' he says, 'to accommodation for twelve weeks' (we used to sleep in an old stone booth, nae bed, nae fire, nae blankets, but a roof certainly over our heads when it rained). 'To oatmeal, yiss, yiss, indeed, twice daily; to milk, yiss, milk has been very expensive this year! Well, Peter,' says he, 'we'll not say anything about that. I make out that you're just clear. Well, maybe hardly, but we'll say—just clear.'

" 'But what aboot me pay?' says I.

" 'I'm telling dee, boy,' he says, 'du has nae pay to get. Isna du gotten dee fill o' aetmeal and milk for three months wi' free lodgings?'

"I nearly grat. 'Have I naething ava?' I said. 'I was hoping to get anyoch for moleskin troosers and a pair o' boots to go to the school in.'

" 'Yea, yea,' says he, 'as for that, moleskin troosers and boots! Du would need that!'

"He peenkled at me, put his glasses back on his broo, gaed twice back and fore ahint the counter. Then he hauled open the money drawer and wapped me out eighteen pence upon the counter. 'Hae,' he says, 'go ower to John Tammason, and tell him to cut dee oot a pair o' rivlins!' And that was what I won for my twal weeks' work—penny ha'penny a week I make it—no what would buy ae fagareek nooadays."

I made sympathetic noises, and then asked if it was about this time that the *Harvest Rose* was wrecked.

"Na, na, Amna I telling you. I was a grown man shairing the corn in Swartaleas, and a breeze o' wind it was, and aye blowing harder, when Andro Smith came down ower the road frae Wasterhus, wi a flecked humlit coo and a peerie broon calf. I said to myself: 'He'll be going to ship them to Lerook, or put them into the Isle.' He was Fullerton's man and did aa the orra work about the farm—a close inbiggit creature he was, and the kind that would as soon tell a lie as look at you, and he had a kind of hunted look about him—they said his wife Mally wore the breeks, and she certainly had a tongue that could clip cloots. Her father afore her was sic sam. He had a tongue that, when he was angry or put out about anything, could raaze you like the back o' a skate.

"Weel, as I was saying, Andro was coming down the road and I thinks: If he's going to put the baess into the Isle, he'll need help and the sooner the better, for the weather is aye getting waur. And good oarsman as he is I doubt if two of us could manage to put them in and row back. And heth! We could row thenadays! Boy, I was listening the other day to this rowing match atween Coxbridge and Kamebridge, and for what a speaking and a spekalation about naething! Sax or eight men row a light scurm o' a boat three mile, and by the time it's ower, maist o' them are lying exoosted—just fairlings done, the announcer says. I wonder what auld Saunders Wunnock (sowl be at rest!) would have thought of them!

"Now there was a man that could row! Kens du, A'm heard me father tell—and I never marked a lie after him— ae fine summer morning Saunders came rowing wi' his peerie boat frae the Ham to the Shore shop to get a bow o' flour. Auld Jeems Johnson was, as it happened clean oot o' meal altogether. Saunders said it didn't matter, he would row over to Gutcher and get it. Jeems says: 'Boy, if du's going, could du take another bow to us, if it'll no bother dee? I hae naebody to send.'

" 'Na, na, boy, it's nae bother ava,' said Saunders, and off he went, rowing steadily awa. But he didna come back.

The day wore on, and by and by it was nine o'clock at night and shop-shutting time, but nae Saunders! Jeems by this time was quite sure that something ill had happened. He couldna leave the shop, he couldna leave the pier, and he kent na what either to do or think.

"Weel, when it was noo past eleven o'clock at night, you'll no hinder him to see a peerie speck far oot to sea to the west o' Sound Gruney, and in less than an hour, in came the peerie whilly wi' Saunders rowing as steadily as when he started.

" 'Saunders Wunnock!' says Jeems, 'Loard be aboot us, whaur's du been aa day?'

" 'Oh,' says he, in his offhanded way, 'when I won to Gutcher, they were oot o' flour there as well, so I just rowed down to Lerook. It was a fine sooth tide. I got the flour, and here it is.' He had rowed about *eighty* miles in less than saxteen hours—for he had to spend sometime in the shops both at Gutcher and Lerook. Noo he wapped Jeems's bow ashore and set off again on the last three miles to Muness, rowing steadily awa. How would Coxbridge and Kamebridge billies, think you, feel after sic a trip when they're exoosted after three miles, far less eighty?

"But while we are speaking about rowing, I have heard o' a crew that wouldna have considered even Saunders Wunnock ony great shakes. Did you ever hear how Jeems Tammason o' Upper Heogaland aince got his Yule Dram?

"Na, weel, it was long afore your time and long afore mine, and naebody noo can remember even Jeems's youngest son that was master of a brig the *Ocean Dawn* in the gold-digging days o' 'forty-nine, and was cassen awa among cannibals and lived as their king for mony years. But I'll may be tell you aboot that later. I aye like to stick to my story and it was aboot auld Jeems his father that I was going to tell you. He was aye in his younger days and even when he grew aulder a great boy for making contact wi' the smugglers, and as a result he was aye mair or less weel provided wi' a' his needs aboot a Yule time, wi' baccy, I mean, at a shilling a pound, and Dutch gin at a shilling a gallon. Oh, dear, a dear!

"There comes a time when a man canna ony longer do as he has done, and that time came to Jeems too. The boys were all grown up and awa, and he and auld Jaikie his wife were noo by themselves in what you know to be an oot o' the way place. Even if he wanted to go to the fishing he had to get the help o' the Bracknigirt men—a braw bit awa—to help him doon and up wi' his boat, for it was a muckle auld patched fourareen, plenty for three men to handle far less ane.

"Well, the night afore Yule Jeems said he would gang doon ower to the beach whaur the boat was, to see that she was snug and shorded properly in the noost, as he thought the weather was likely to be waur afore it was better.

"It was dark when he reached the boat, and he made aa snug inside and ootside o' her, when he hears the tramp trample and the scruffling o' heavy steps coming ower the shingly ayre atween the Holmsound and Moula. Noo, it was a lonesome neighbourhood as I've said, and it was ower near the bad days o' the pressgang for a man to put himself in the way o' strangers at night, if he could be withoot, and Jeems stepped quietly into the boat and smooted himself awa as snugly as he could in the stern o' her.

"Soon he heard voices o' men speaking loudly among themselves, and to his horror they stopped beside the boat. 'We'll hae to tak the auld man's boat to fetch the drink,' one o' them said in a voice as loud and coorse as a looder-horn: 'There's no anither near the place, and it's no that far to Norrowa'. Doon wi her, boys!'

"Before Jeems could stir, even if he had had the power to do so, as he had no, the boat's keel crunched doon the shingle, four great giants o' men jumped on board and oot they rowed roond Moula at a great rate as it seemed to

Jeems. They slackened speed for a moment, taking off their jackets and making themselves comfortable, Jeems judged.

"Then ane o' them cried: 'Noo,

> *Row strong and wi' a will*
> *Twal mile at every vill* (stroke),'

and in a minute or twa, it seemed nae mair, the boat's nose grated on shingle. The men spanged oot and went away. Jeems, after a bit, cautiously lifted his head. Nearby there were great dark cliffs and mountains on baith sides, and doon between them through a valley came a great burn or river rushing as violently as Bluemull Soond in a spring tide. The boat lay at the end o' a low shingly spit o' land, and Jeems could dimly descry atween himself and the distant skyline great trees standing on the slopes like birse on a swine's back. But soon he heard the noise and trampling o' the men returning and crouched back in his place again. Then followed the thuds o' half a dozen heavy objects being dropped into the boat, which was now pushed off and turned seaward. Aince mair the great booming voice roared oot.

> " '*Row strong and wi' a will*
> *Twal mile at every vill,*'

and in next to nae time they were back at land and the boat was dragged up and shorded on the beach. When he felt his auld boat was safe back in her place Jeems begood to pluck up his courage again. He rose to his feet, extended his arms and hands in front o' him, and crying oot: 'The Lord haud His hand aboot me and mine,' fell forward clutching.

"There was a dead silence and for a long time he lay, no daring to open his eyes. When he did so at last, he found himself lying on his face in the 'shot' of the boat, his hands and arms aroond a fine four gallon keg o' Norrowa brandy which the Finn men had had to leave behind when Jeems sained himself.

"Yea, truly it's a tale hard to believe as you say, but I'll say the same to you as Jeems said to Jaikie. When he came in and set doon the keg on the table, she stood, een and mooth open, listening to his tale and leaning wi' her hands and arms aroond it. When he finished she cried oot: 'Oh, Jeems, Jeems! for sic a story. I can hardly believe it.' He said: 'So, joy! The hank is in your ain hands, mak you a better o' it then.'

"There's no sae mony kegs o' brandy noo, nor men to drink them. The rising generation think they hae a good drink noo if they hae a swittle o' brew that lies as heavy as a cauld tattie on an empty stammick!

"But I mind auld Peter o' Storataft telling me o' ae Godsend that he had when he was a boy. You ken every Newerday the young men and some even that werena sae young—auld whiskered sixern-skippers-used to gather on the Links o' Lund to play the ba'. It wasna exactly like the fitba nooadays; there were nae teams; every man played for himsel. The ba' was kicked high in the air, and he was the man who could catch it when it came doon, and kick it up again. Naebody keepit ony score o' coorse—it was sufficient pleasure for a man to ken he had got a good kick at it, and to ken at the same time that he had deprived his neighbour o' that same pleasure for the time being!

"Weel, at the time o' his story Peter was coming on for fourteen years of age, the youngest o' five stately brether, and this Newer morning he said naething aboot his intention but set off to play the ba' wi' the rest o' them. Oot ower below the muckle hoose o' Lund they begood to play and in racing for the ba' wha should he deprive o' it just be inches but his ain auldest brither Lowrie!

"And Lowrie jamp at him at wance! 'What are you doing here, you whalp? Get awa home before I cloot your lugs for

you, coming here among men and leaving your father and
mother wi' naebody in the hoose to help them wi' onything.' The ither brithers joined in and narked at him, just
like David's brithers when he gaed doon to see the fighting
wi' the Philistines in the valley of Elah!

"Maybe Peter didna hae the spunk o' David. Onyway,
David remained to cut off Goliath's heid, and Peter, no
very far frae greeting, had to mak his wye as unobtrusively
as he could awa frae the players, and gaed slowly hame-
wards. Noo there had been a bitterly hard frost of some
days, but it had thawed through the night, and the day was
actually warm, for a Newerday that is.

"As he crossed the Burga sands on his wye he happened
to notice that a bit o' the sandy bank o' the burn had
slipped doon and there was the roonded edge o' something
sticking oot o' the new face o' the bank. Well, Peter wasna
exactly in a hurry to get back to the hoose, and boylike
began purling wi' a bit o' stick roond this object to see what
it was. It took him some time, as, except for the end, it was
buried under twa feet o' hard packed sand, but in the lang
o' the length, he had it a' clear, and was delighted to see as
bonny a little wooden keg as you could picture—oak staves
by the look o' it, and neat beautifully finished green metal
hoops aroond it. And (a thing that made his blude tingle
wi' excitement!) when he lifted it up it was very heavy and
swankled! It wasna to bid him hurry hame wi' his find!

"His father duly admired the keg and they decided to
find out what was inside, so wi' the help o' a broag they
bored a hole through the bung and anither at ae end close
to the leggings and poured oot a cupfu o' the liquid. The
smell was good, but nane o' the twa dared to taste for they
had an unco dread o' poison. It might kill them stark deid!
But on the ither hand it might be the very thing for the
New Year! Peter's father was sair perplexed for a time
and then he slapped his leg and laughed. 'The very thing,'
says he.

"He searched till he found a little bottle that would hold about twa gills, ran it fu' o' the liquid and corked it.

" 'Noo, Peter,' says he, 'listen carefully. When I paid the rent at Hallowmass I was fifteen shillings short and I promised the laird that come what may he should have the money by Newerday. This very night I meant to send Lowrie ower the hill wi' the money. Noo, you'll tak the money and this flask too in your pocket. Mind and ask for the Laird himsel' and dinna tak no for an answer. He'll likely offer you a dram since its Newerday, and then ye'll kind o' shyly offer him ane. If he says no, just ask him to taste upon it for luck's sake. Watch his face carefully and listen to what he says. If he splutters and spits it oot and speaks aboot poison, just you be horrified and say ye must have taen the wrang bottle wi' the calf's medicine.'

"Peter set off on his errand thinking that he was having a fine Newer day after a'. But you may be sure he shook in his shoes, when, after everything had happened as his father had said it would, he came to the point o' offering the laird a dram. 'My father said you werena to be offended but to tak it wi' his blessing.' He used to brag that his hand didna shake when he ran oot a glass fu, and the laird set it to his heid and tilted it off like a man. Then he gasped and the water came to his een and he spluttered: 'Coneyak! Faith, boy, that's good coneyak! Whaur did your father get a drop o' that stuff?'

"Peter felt as high as a hoose; he made some evasive answer and filled the glass again, asking the laird if he would be good enough to hae a dram frae him too. No only did he do so, but after it was doon, he looked at Peter and he looked at the fifteen shillings on his desk, and then shoved ane o' them ower to Peter saying: 'Hae, boy! There's your New Year's hansel!'

"Peter hurried awa hame as prood as a dog wi' twa tails to gie his auld man the good news, aye saying ower to himself: 'Coneyak, good coneyak!' So you can imagine he never forgat that Newerday, though I never heard that Lowrie or ony o' the ither brether were ever the wiser or better o' his discovery that day!

"But to get back to what I was telling you. Andro wi' his coo and calf stops when he comes forenenst where I was, and I hails him and axed what news was wi' him. 'Oh, same auld thing,' he says, 'plenty o' work and some folk never pleased.' That I could well believe for his maister auld Fullerton was a driver and so was the mistress. You'll hardly believe it but they had nineteen head o' kye on the byre—and they aye killed and salted one for the winter. They made their own cheese, too. If you're ever up at the auld hoose, you'll see the great stone cheese-press still standing at the south corner. And it was real cheese, too, not like this dowed saepy dirt in the shops nooadays. " 'Whaurs du taking the baess?' I axed him and he leuch.

" 'He wants them put into the Isle,' he says. 'I told him that it wouldna be a day for it, but du kens what he is—he listens to naebody, and it's worsenin' in the weather.'

"And so it was, for it was noo blowing so hard that the corn was slanting ower so that I couldna get shorn; and the soond o' the wind hushing among it was like that o' the seas breaking on the sands o' Sanook.

" 'Na, na,' I says. 'It's no a day for the Isle or anything else, and A'm thinking he'll be waur afore he's better. Bind du the coo yonder, and come in and dip dee a start. It's no even a day for sharing, for less mair.'

" 'A'll be ower blide to linn me,' says he and wi' that we started oot for the house.

"As we wandered hame ower I says.

" 'It fairlies me if we're no in for something oot o' the ordinar' in the way o' weather.'

" 'Boy, what makes dee think that?' says he. 'I thought that noo wi' the new mune we might have a dry sook for a bit.'

" 'Weel, I'se tell dee,' says I. 'I mind me grandfather

K.

saying that afore the great gale o' 'thirty-two, when aa the
sixerns were lost, although it was fine weather the day afore,
yet there was a strange soond and cry o' the sea on the
Kiosteens, a soond he said that tightened a man's throat by
its awful ootpouring o' loneliness and desolation. And in
'fifty-six when the sixerns frae Burrafirt and Norook were
lost in the Strings o' Skaw, again upon the height o'
summer, didna folk hear the day afore, the same weary
waesome cry aroond the Holm o' Skaw? Wha kens? If a
peerie boat, made by the helpless hands o' man, at times
gets a sowl, or a kind o' life at onyrate, and battles sairly
for that life wi' the angry sea, as A'm seen it do, mony and
mony a time, why shouldna the great sea, created by the
awful hand o' the Almighty, no hae feeling and life o' a kind
too?

" 'Weel, aboot that neither you nor I nor ony man knows
for certain. But the streen when I was at the craigs oot at
Twaemennskuddie, though it was as fine a night for fishing
as the heart o' man could wish for, the sea was restless on
the rocks o' the ness, soughing and mourning like a hurt
bairn that greets itself to sleep. Even the klaag o' the
birds showed that they were restless and uneasy aboot
something I wasna aware o'. And last night, too, I had a
dream that makes me think the weather will be waur for a
while.'

" 'A dream,' says he wi' a lauch. 'I never heard o' ony o'
our folk having a dream that came true unless it was
Joannie Magnie. And he wasna really our folk, for he was
my grand uncle Alex's stepson. A'm heard our folk saying
that when he was a young sheeld, he never bothered wi' the
lasses and seemed likely to grow into an auld bachelor,
when ae morning he mentioned to the auld folk that he
had had a queer dream. He had dreamed he was standing
in the Muckle Kirk right up forenenst the poopit aa by
himself, and suddenly twa lasses as like as preens stood ane
on each side, and the minister suddenly appeared frae

somewhere and began to read the marriage service; he was in a nasty fix as he didna have the least idea whether he should turn to the lass on his left or the lass on his right, and he waukened up wi' the annoyance and the gluff o' it.

" ' "It was a horrible dream," he said, "they were bonny kindly lasses, that they were, but ower exactly alike." 'They must a been twins surely,' my uncle said, 'though I kenna whaur du'll find twins, frae Skaw to Moula."

" ' "Wait you," says his wife (Maggie Boyne her name was, and she came from the north end o' the isle, and was second cousin to my wife's mother), "wait you, doesna Gibbie o' Ballista hae twa upgrown twin lasses? A'm heard o' them and naebody has aught to say against either their looks or their behaviour—two fine lasses everybody says."

" 'Joannie Magnie just grointed and gaed on wi' his breakfast, but afore the end o' the hairst he's made acquaintance wi' the lasses, and fower years afterwards (it took him that time to make up his mind atweist them) he stood afore the poopit and married ane o' them, wi' th ither ane acting as best maid.'

"Well, by this time we had come in and were sitting waiting for a cup o' tea and a bite in our mooths, when he said: 'But what was your dream aboot, Peter?'

" 'My dream,' says I, 'is ane that generally comes true in a way, but it takes me to understand the way. For aa dreams in my opinion hae meanings, but needna hae the same meaning for everybody. Of course some dreams are well enough kent to need nae interpretation. I needna tell dee aboot seeing ships or boats travelling over land, or aboot teeth loose or coming oot or sic-like (Guid be aboot us aa!) Na, it wisna ony o' that, but A'm noticed aa my life that if I dream aboot peats or peat stacks it's going to be bad weather. Well, I dreamed I'd gone oot to the stack for a kishiefu o' peats and was filling awa at the open end when I seemed to hear a noise at the far end o' the stack. When I came roond the stack here was a stranger man filling awa at his kishie frae ane o' the corners I'd had such a care and tryst bigging. You can say wi' a warrant that I was far frae pleased and axed him at wance what he was doing— did he know this was my stack, and had he no more sense than to raab doon the weather corner o' ony man's sair-coft winter-stack, but he just looked up and said: "No spake English," and gaed on filling his kishie just as indifferently as if I had said it was a fine day. I made for him at wance and he swapped the kishie on his back, the peats dropping oot, and awa he gaed wast ower.'

" 'That's not a good dream,' says Andro. 'Du's going to loss something.'

" 'It's no that way I look at it,' I says, 'the peats of course is bad weather, there's nae doot aboot that. But for anything else, my dreams aye go by opposites, so I'd sooner dream o' a man taking peats than bringing peats. Na, it's mair likely someone coming frae the westard, bringing something, but no in a kishie, true du me!' "

"The something would likely be the *Harvest Rose*," I ventured, trying to bring him back.

"Surely. Amna I telling you. Andro and me was sitting having a smoke after something in our mooths when the first that we saw was Robbie Coutts that baed in Millagord coming wi' a great swap upon him—you'll mind his son muckle Joannie, though he was frae his second marriage, wi' a Yell wumman. I mind Robbie aye used to say that Solomon kent something when he spoke aboot strange women, and he aye had a great word, 'Sel doe, sel hae!' meaning, I think, that the man who commits some folly has to put up wi' the consequence o' it. Weel, Robbie was in through the door and standing on the floor afore we could begin to think whaur he was making for, and afore we could say a word, he bursts oot. 'Boys, boys, there's a ship driven ashore at Heddiwick. Tammy was up through Akersgill after the almark and he saw her gang broadside on the Fless

—a three-masted ship she is. He's run aa the way back wi'
the news. Are you coming?'

" 'Just wait till I get me seaboots and a bit o' line," I
says. Robbie, you know, never had much forethought aboot
onything. But weel I kent that a bit o' line is aye handy.
We werena long setting oot I can tell dee, Robbie and Andro
and me, face a wind aa the way and as muckle as you could
do to make headway against it. 'Haste you, haste you!'
said Robbie, 'by this time every man besooth the Strodie
will be there unless the bedrals and the Whalback men.' "

He laughed quietly and took some time slowly fashioning
a spill and lighting his pipe. But I was not to be drawn and
he was forced to continue. "Of course you know the way
that saying came aboot."

"What saying?" I asked.

"Everybody but the Whalback men."

"I don't know," said I, "unless it's because they are out
of sight of the sea and away from the main road so that they
don't hear of things quickly."

"Na, na, there's far mair in it than that. It was in my
grandfather's time that the saying began. A Norroway
ship, the *Snakir*, I think she was caaed, drave ashore wi'
an aesterly wind right into the gio o' Cunnisgirt and the
second mate was killed by a spar falling inboard when she
strack. Mercifully, the forefit o' her jammed right in to the
peerie gio and with the ebbing water the rest o' them got
ashore, and even managed to bring the dead man with them
rowed up in a new topsail. By the time they were aa safely
ashore the darkness was beginning to set in. It was the
month of November. So for the time being they left the
corpse under the bank's broo and were taen here and there
to the crofts to get a bite in their mooths and dry claes.
Aa men frae roond aboot had been at the gio ever sin the
ship strack, and noo aa men were gane taking the Nor-
wegians hame wi' them.

"Weel, you'll no hinder the Whalback men to come in the

first o' the darkness. They hadna heard o' the wrack in time, but fower o' them had made it up to go together to see if they could find anything. Great aevirs o' men they were, Tammie and Robbie Rasmusson, breither than baed in Roequoy, 'A'm heard that they could baith easily lift a man standing on the mooth of a shovel) and Gibbie and Peter Anderson o' Gerdroos.

"When they came, as I said, it was nearly dark, and there wasna sae muckle left to find. Everything that had seemed worth while was saved and lying abune the banks, and it was mair by accident than onything else that one o' them stumbled below the banks ower a large bundle wrapped up in a sail. There werena sae mony lectric blinkies thenadays, but by trivilling they made oot that it was carefully tied and snugged by, so it had to be something mair than ordinary veelable, and the fower o' them wi' never a word looked at one another and picked it up.

"Off they set, and a very long hard road they had afore them, up ower the face o' the Vordhill, whaur you mind the outlook men were in the wartime, and by the Gorstie o' Sobul. You ken yon long owergrown auncient raabit daek that you can trace half the length o' the isle. Man, I mind at the skule auld Whitie had been reading to us about the siege o' Jerusalem oot o' Joseephus, and was questioning us after aboot what he had read. 'And what happened at last to Jerusalem?' he axed peerie Obadiah o' Umbit. 'Oh,' says he, right away, 'it was just like the Gorstie o' Sobul, no wan stone left upon another.'

"Weel, you can imagine it was some time afore they got as far as the Gorstie, carrying their heavy burden, and stumbling in the darkness; then roond the west side o' Trollamires—surely the last place Gude ever made. I mind me losing a fower-year-old mare right in the middle o' that mire. It was in the hard winter o' 'eighty-nine and she had gone ower far and stuck. It was hard frost ower aa the land when I sought her, and it had lasted for near a fortnight, and there she was, puir brute, just head and neck abune the ice, deid and frozen hard as a grey stone.

"By the time they had won their way to the harder, firmer ground beyond they were very tired, and Gibbie or ane o' the others said: 'Boys, let us linn for a bit here on this knowe.' (If you're ever there you'll know the knowe by the peerie bubbling spring that comes oot anunder a muckle white stone close by.) 'Let us linn us a start, and open the package and divide what is in it. It'll carry easier, and we'll see what we're doing noo the mune is risen.'

"So they cut the tows and unrowed the sail, and then in the munelight for a lang lang time just sat looking in the dead man's face!

"If you find the place you'll notice near the spring twa stones marking the grave; and that's the reason that the Whalback men never gaed aboot the banks again.

"Weel, as I was saying, Robbie and Andro and me set oot heid a wind up through Akersgill—you'll ken it, the very last place that the trows to my knowledge were seen or said to be seen in Unst. If it's no a true story the lee is no mine. Yea, it's no sae very lang sin syne—my grand-father could mind Ollie the fiddler that used to bide in Heogaland.

"He was a noted fiddler, and was in great demand at every rant in the sooth end o' the isle, and noo he had been invited to play at a wedding in the north Wasting, and by his tale he set oot in guid time sometime in the after-noon.

"As he came up through Akersgill the mist steekit roond him like a box, and he could hardly see his hand in front of him. He sat doon to wait a bit to see if it wadna clear up, took a dram oot o' his bottle and snugged his coat aroond him. Then he began to think o' the wedding and thought he would try a spring or twa to see that his fingers were as soople as he would like them, for he had been bigging at a daek aa day. So he played awa a start wi his een closed

as was his wont, Meg Merrilees, and the Brunt Scones o'
Voe, and the Sailor ower the Ruiftrees and siclike.

"When he opened his een he stopped playing, and just
sat and looked aa roond him, and aa roond him, while a
cauld grue ran up his rig, and he could feel the hair on the
back of his neck stirring and bristling wi' fear. For he was
sitting in the very middle o' a ring o' peerie auld faced
whiskered men aa preenked up the same way. He said they
had tight greeny coloured juppies snug fitting roond the
neck, grey breeks no unlike moleskin, peaky hats wi' wide
brims on their heids, and on their feet dark hairy rivlins.
They were aa just sitting gazing at him, but it was their
een, dark, bright and piercing that frightened him maist—
mair like whitrits, een he said than human beings. They
never said a word, but as he gazed and gazed, first ane and
then anither bared their bright white teeth like girning
dogs and then suddenly the whole ring wi' one movement
gae a peerie jump forward and sat aince mair girning.

"Something seemed to say to him 'Play, man, play,'
and he set the fiddle under his chin, closed his een, and
leashed awa at the Blue Yowe and Kail and Knockit Corn
and what no until he was tired. Then he thought I was
just dreaming yon time and opened his een slowly. There
they were aa sitting as he had last seen them, every ee
upon him, but they were no nearer at onyrate. He just
looked and looked but in a short time he saw their teeth
again, and suddenly the whole ring aince mair made a
peerie jump forward. This time though, he kent what to
do, took up his fiddle again and played like mad.

"But he didna close his een tightly although he made a
pretence o' it, and as long as he played, there they sat
nodding their heids and moving their hands and feet in
time to the music. When he stopped, as though they were
waiting for a sign, they aa made their peerie jump forward
aince mair. And aince mair Ollie had to fiddle for dear
life, wi' the warm sweat dripping frae his eyebrows and the

cauld mist swirling roond the circle o' the peerie folk, but
never coming atwen him and them.

"Sae it gaed on and on, and aye the ring drew nearer and
nearer, and, weel he kent, he felt it in every atom o' his
being that the moment they touched him he would be lost,
dragged into some knowe frae the light o' day for evermore, or torn in pieces and devoured by their awesome
teeth."

"But," I interrupted, "I never heard of the trows being
carnivorous."

"What? Oh, yea, that were they—carnivorous, sheep-
ivorous, and even sometimes dogivorous. But as I was
saying, Ollie begood to think that his last day was come.
He could noo hardly move either arm or fingers, and found
himsel playing slow mournful tunes like the 'Last Sheaf o'
Hairst,' and 'Daa's Auld Boat.' Even that failed him at
last—fiddle and bow together slipped oot o' his hands, and
he just fell back ower. And in a moment it seemed they
were upon him. He was plucked and pinched this way and
that, and then he felt great teeth fasten into the ba' o' his
leg and tear and tear. He cried oot: 'Guid be aroond and
gaird me!'

"The plucking ceased and aa was still but after a start
it begood again gently and peerie ways at his left leg. He
opened his een and there was his peerie collie Bob that he
had left at home sitting near his feet wi' his heid tilted a
bit to ae side, and a look o' concern in his een, as if he was
saying: 'What ails dee that du's lying here?'

"And then he saw a thing that surprised him even mair.
The sun was high in the heevins ower the Klett o' Fetlar.
It must be late in the morning! But what morning? What
morning?

"Wi' that he sprang to his feet, took up his fiddle and
bow, baith damp wi' the dew, and, nae thought noo o' the
wedding left, hurried home. Weel he kent that ae night
wi' the trows might be half a lifetime to mortal men. By

this time wife and bairns and kye and grice and even the sheep might aa be nae mair, maybe no even a ruif ower his heid might noo be his to caa his ain! Stiff and auld as he already felt himself to be in every limb, he begood to run till he came in sight o' his hoose. Yea, the ruif was still on, and the blue reek was standing straight up frae the but lum in a calm and lovely simmer morning!

"He slackened his pace for a moment but then as a thought struck him looked at the dog to see if there was ony odds on him. He couldna honestly say he saw muckle difference but of course dogs sometimes didna change very much for years. He couldna bear to think ony longer; he could only just run and run until the blude sang and bummled in his lugs and his briest was bursting. Until he came to the open door, whaur he stopped to draw his breath, then plunged like a man that dives into deep water, right in over the threshold.

"His wife, Mima, looked up frae whaur she sat rocking the cradle and said: 'Is du back already? He's surely been a short wedding.' Thenadays, as you know, twa days and nights o' festivity were usual on such an occasion. 'Short or lang,' says he, 'I never won till him. But this I do know, A'm a blithe and happy man to be home again.'

"And to the day o' his death he seldom ever gaed oot o' the hoose again when there was mist aboot, or likely to be mist; and he never, never, set foot in Akersgill mair, mist or no mist!

"But we were hardly thinking of trows and siclike that day as we hurried on as best we could, Robbie a peerie bit ahead in his excitement, but never getting very far in front for aa that, Andro and me blithe enough to let him break the wind for us, for we had the best part o' fower mile o' gait to go ower the hills. Though the truth is that we would have made little o' it, if we had had even a langer distance to go. For little we thought o' either fower mile or twinty-fower. Noo, if a youth sets oot for a rant or a concert or what no, it's either a motor bike or a car or bus that conveys him, even if it be less than twa mile o' gait.

"Peace be wi' the days that a man's ain feet carried him by land whaur he would be, even if it were forty or saxty mile. Man, folk canna walk nooadays! I was speaking to young Lowrie Edwardson the streen and he was bragging that last year on a walking tour wi' some sooth chums they had done twinty mile a day for a week.

" 'Twinty mile,' said I, 'man, as late as my own recollection in 1875, we had but ae postman for Unst and Yell. Davie Johnson o' Haroldswick would set out twice a week collecting on his way the ootgoing letters frae Baltasound and Oesound, cross the Scord to Snarravoe, whaur he was rowed across Blue Mull Sound to Cullivoe. There he would lift the ootgoing mail, touch along Gutcher and Mid Yell post offices for their letters, and in the end hand over his mail bag at Ulsta, a total distance in ae day o' about forty miles, carrying the mails o' aa Unst and Yell on his back. Neist morning, wi' the incoming mail in a bag, he would retrace his road, delivering on the way his letters at Mid Yell, Gutcher, Cullivoe, Oesound and Baltasound. And he had naebody to help him, unless at times as he grew older his dowter would come the twelve mile frae Haroldswick to Snarravoe to meet him on his hameward way.

" 'They tell me that Unst noo gets eighty bags o' mails a week for itsel, though noo there's no half the folk to get them. Think you, are we eighty times either wiser or better off than we were in 1875? I canna see it. We used to say o' a man that had plenty o' schemes and plans, but never did onything, that he was aa heid and nae hands, but it seems to me that in nae long time noo folk will hae neither hands nor feet. As to their heids I'll say naething but this. If the young folk noo ken the day o' the week and the airt o' the wind that's just aboot the sum o' their knowledge; and they mind naething. When I was a young man it was nae uncommon thing for onybody wi' an ordinary memory to be able to repeat word for word when he came back from the Kirk on the Sawbath day, the hale twa oors' discoorse o' a minister like Dr. Ingram, even if it had, as it sometimes did, a thirteenthly, finally, and in conclusion.

"'And nae winder! A man might hae sax miles to travel ower the hills frae the Muckle Kirk on his way hame, and time enough to chew the cud o' meditation as he gaed. Aye, they had lang sermons. I mind Jamie Peterson o' Muness telling me that when he was a young man he used to go every Sawbath to the kirk in Baltasound, and as he had a lang gait in front o' him he used to speak alang the door at Boitnigirt as he gaed.

" 'Weel, ae day he fand the folk there in a great steer and commotion, as a bairn was just on the point of arriving into this weary world. So he just merely spoke at the door and wished them well, and continued on his way. He arrived at the kirk and settled doon to listen to the service, and afore the sermon was ended folk arrived frae Boitnigirt wi' the new born bairn to be christened!

" 'You see it was considered the right thing to do, to christen a bairn as soon as ever possible, for if it died unchristened—well, folk just couldna bear to think about it. And whenever such a thing happened, for of course it happened noo and then, they aye used to bury such peerie things whaur the raindraps frae the kirk roof would dreep upon them. Though it might do nae guid, it couldna do ony hairm they thought, and as it in a kind o' way comforted the bereaved, the minister, wise man, let it pass. But my tale shows you no only hoo little folk thought o' a lang walk, but the length o' the sermons they baith listened to and could remember.

" 'Weel, for us the fower mile ower the hills and moors would a been naething ava in the way o' exertion if it hadna been for the wind that was blowing nearly as hard as I can remember—a roaring flying gale wi' swaffs noo and again that fairly staggered us. It was nae use trying to exchange a word; for ae thing we couldna a heard what was said, and for anither we needed aa the breath we had. But as Ertie o' Soerhus was wont to say, if a man was doing nothing else he could aye be thinking.

" 'I kenna what Robbie and Andro were thinking aboot, but it was rinning through my mind that it would be naething short o' providential and a Gude's mercy if the ship could be bringing a cargo o' wid. The barn ruif could do wi' some new couples, and the wife had been at me for years to plenish wi' wid, at onyrate the ben-end. But you ken hoo time passes—it had aye been pitten off and pitten off. Maybe noo, I was thinking to mesel, the chance is come at last.

" 'But wi' wracks and their cargoes it's the same as wi' everything else—hardly ever at aa points does onything tally wi' your expectations, and baith wracks and cargoes can be very disappointing. I mind when a great muckle widden sailing ship, the *Cape Rhy*, they caaed her, drave ashore upon the taing o' Noostigirt—it was in the hinder end o' September in the year 'eighty and sair trouble and wet hides men had in getting the crew ashore in safety, as there were neither lifeboats nor rocket paratus at that time —but it was aboot her cargo I was speaking. What think you was it? Naething but fresh water ice and empty grain bags. She was boond for Sooth America for wheat her skipper said, and he lamented and better lamented the loss o' his freshwater ice; so much so that auld Tammason couldna bear it at last and cried oot: "What the —— just yon place—did it matter whether the ice was freshwater or saltwater? It was nae use to onybody." But the grain-bags, the truth is, did come handy for covering the bare waas that werena uncommon in the but ends o' maist hooses.

" 'Na, they werena used for peat bags; aa man had his ain kishies and could make them too, and his hurl forbye.

" 'But speaking o' bags reminds me o' the maist curio

cargo I ever heard tell o'. It's a lang time sin syne but my grandfather used to tell the story as he had heard it frae the auld men.

" 'Ae day wi' a norwest gale a peerie ship was seen drifting helplessly broadside straight for the Vair oot fram frae Lundawick. It turned oot later that her rudder had been unshipped and broken by a heavy sea, and there she was just a helpless log wallowing upon the pitiless face o' the ocean. The crew tried to launch their peerie cobble but it smashed in bruck alangside. Noo the skipper warned them that their case was hopeless, and their last day come, and they just stood helpless on deck waiting for the end as the ship neared the breaking seas round the skerry.

" 'It must a been by the providence o' the Almighty, for she came in safe through the narrow gap atween the Boerre and the Vair, half oot o' sight in the white spunedrift, through a gap so narrow that wi' the breaking seas it seemed impossible, and drave ashore in Lundawick. You can still see the black rock in the middle o' the sands whaur at last they got a hawser on shore and made fast, and in the end aa the men were safe and sound ashore too. They were foreigners, ane and aa, and were made welcome and led awa to the hooses roond aboot for food and dry claes.

" 'Very soon wi' the great sea that was running the ship brook up, and great bales o' stuff came plopping oot o' her, and bobbing ashore. Men would rin into the sea to the oxters to grab them and get them safe ashore, and row them to the top o' the sands abune the flude mark, then run back and save another bale, and so they ran back and fore for oors till in the end the bales were safe and snug abune the highest tide mark, everyman's pile of course— separate for itsel. For it wasna a case o' share and share alike thenadays—what a man earned for himsel was his ain and naebody else's.

" 'When naething mair was coming ashore for the time being, they cut the seizings and began to open the bales, and in a hundred years you couldna guess what was in them—nae silks or sateens, claith or claes, neither adornment for the ooter man, nor comfort for the inner—naething but white feathers—peerie soft white feathers!

" 'For a time they thought this could only be the ooter packing for something extra fine and precious, and dived and dived their airms abune the elbucks, their fingers purling and trivilling; they pooed oot and huved awa gawpenfus and gawpenfus, so that the steuch o' feathers raise and floated awa up the daal like a wintry moorikav o' snow. But in the end the deil ither thing was in the bales but just the feathers. It turned oot when the crew and the hame men got to understand ane anither by and by that the ship—she was caaed the Fivla—was frae Iceland wi' a cargo o' swans' doon.' "

"It would have made a soft bed," I ventured to interject.

"Maybe it would, right enough, but it didna. Folk had nae time to bother much aboot saft beds. Na, if a man had a windling or twa o' strae to lay benon the bottomdeals o' his bed, he was comfortable withoot swans' doon or ony ither doon. But it was the sacking roond the feathers that brought the story to my mind. It did come in handy for sticking up roond the waas—it maybe wasna sae bonny to look at as some o' the flooert papering you canna afford noo to buy in the shops, but it served the same purpose and had the advantage o' lasting longer, forbye being a hantle cheaper.

"But noo, where was I? Oh, yea, I mind. By the time we had come roond the end o' the Snarravoe loch and faced the brae we could hardly make headway at all in spite o' the fact that we were to some extent in shelter from the wind. And when we reached the top and Snabroch was afore us, the wind was like something solid, as if you were wading to the shoulders in saat water—you could taste the saat on your lips although we were the best part o' a mile frae the sea—and there was a roar in it, unbelievable unless you had heard it. It was mair a scream like what you might imagine the Deil gave when he sprang through the hoose o' Lund. Man, it's queer the stories folk believed afore this. There are nae ploys noo at Hallowmass but it was different in the auld days.

"My grandfather used to tell us of the great times they had when he was a boy, puing the kailstock, fathoming the screws, treading the harrows, drapping the clew, sifting siller, wetting the sark sleeve and what no and what no. He aye used to laugh when he told us aboot Janey, Bartle's daughter. It was a very auld story. She was said to hae been a kind o' general servant, ootdoor and indoor in the Laird's hoose, and was getting to the time o' life when if she wanted a man, it was time she did something aboot it, for although she was a fine worker, healthy and kind in her way, and as strong as a horse, the truth was she resembled a horse in mair than her strength; she was kind o' horsey-faced wi' lang-boned cheeks and big teeth.

"Weel, onyway, on Hallowmass Eve, you'll no hinder her to make up her mind to sift siller atween the twa open doors o' the kitchen o' Lund. What way did they do it? There's naething difficult aboot doing it. You sit in a room wi' twa doors open to the outer air; you hae three sieves and you sift widdergaits a handfu o' siller frae the one sieve to the second, then to the third, and go through this performance three times. Your back is turned to the doors and you keep looking in a looking glass placed in front of you. The feyness or appearance of your future partner in life (if you're going to have a partner) will come in the one door and go oot the ither. It's no a thing though I ever heard o' a man trying (generally, I think, they ken aa aboot their partners soon enough!) But the lasses noo and again would try things like that.

"Janey had settled hersel comfortably in the darkening on a creepie stool and was leidfully sifting awa looking in the mirror, when an awful almighty roar o' wind got up aroond the hoose, and an enormous black man bounded in through the one door, gave an awful yell, and bounded oot the ither, leaving ahint him a strong reek o' sulphur, and on one o' the flagstones the deep mark o' a cloven hoof! Janey's shrieks brought everybody rinning and when she managed to gasp oot her story, the servants ane and aa just refused to enter the kitchen again until men came and removed the flagstone, and the priest had sprinkled holy water roond aboot!

"Weel, lot's o' folk believed the story and lots o' folk believed it was the De'il himself, cloven hoof and all, but my grandfather said he didna believe a word o' it, for, said he, ony man or deil for that matter, that bounded in and saw naething o' Janey but the reflexion o' her face in the looking glass, would have turned back and bounded oot through the same door he had come in by!"

It was at this moment, however, that a great misfortune befell us. My narrator happened to stand up and look out the window, and turning quickly with a measure of excitement remarked: "Look you, you hae better een than I hae, isna yon a motor boat coming roond the end o' the Isle. Yea, that it is, and she's coming in to the pier. It's the Skerries boat that comes noo and then wi' fish. We'll hae to make for the pier to see what he has to-day."

As he was speaking he had drawn on his boots and now reached for his muffler, cap, and pipe, and we were outside in no time, for I had no option but to follow. I was anxious enough to see the catch, and as we had more than a mile to go still hoped I might get the information about the *Harvest Rose*. He was in story telling mood and I might never have another chance to call up so to speak "him who left half told the story of Cambuscan bold." I said I hoped he would have time to finish the story.

"Whaur was I?" said he, as we went down the road. "Oh, well, never mind! When we at last reached Heddiwick, aa the banks and beach was lined wi' men frae aa the sooth parish and farther. Oh, doel and when! There's no sae mony noo! I mind seeven sixerens fishing frae the Wasteen beach, twa frae the Eastside, two or three frae the Hamm, forbye the boats frae the Shore aa at the same time. We would be oot to sea forty miles afore sunset on Monanday and back again some time afore the end o' the week, wi' great hauls o' ling and tusk and cod. Oh, boy, there were generally fish in the sea and nae hain thenadays, and no only in simmer, when sometimes we would come ashore wi' twinty-five hundredweight or mair o' fine fish for the week's catch, but sometimes in winter too.

"Did you ever hear o' the great clack fishing o' 'seventy-six? Weel I mind it, as well I may, for if ever the hand o' Providence was openly revealed it surely was then, when man's need was the sairest. For 'seventy-five had truly been a bad year—baith on the sea wi' calm still days and little sign o' fish at ony o' the kent meads, and bad on the land, for it was a year when nae rain fell frae the month o' March till November.

"It was the year when Dr. Smith o' Clivocast opened a knowe no far frae his hoose, and fand the skeleton o' a man in armour—some auld Viking maybe. Frae aa A'm heard aboot them, they didna brook being meddled wi', alive or deid, and there was some speaking aboot what the doctor had done. Folk didna like it; they said that little guid could come o' disturbing a man's last rest, whaever he was, or whatever he'd been. It was nae business o' onybody, even a doctor, to be howking awa among deid men's banes.

"And true it was that naething prospered aa that year. Sae muckle sae that by the coming o' the New Year the merchant himsel was in despair, and if the merchant canna make a living wha can? Weel, on the 28th o' Janiwar he came doon to the shop on the Setterday morning and telled his foreman that he was closing up for good and all; it was nae use struggling on; aa man roond aboot owed him money up to the neck, wi' nae prospect o' ever clearing himsel.

"This was bad news for the foreman too; he had his ain troubles. 'Can ye no carry on,' says he, 'if it was but for a fortnight. Times are bound to change for the better.' 'Weel,' said the merchant, 'so be it! I'll take your words for a sign, and another fortnight it shall be.'

"The boats had been working awa noo and again at the clack, but of coorse mair to get something to boil in the pot, than to sell, for as you know onything you get frae the sea in winter is sair coft, and the weather since Yule had been stormy and wet. But wi' better weather coming six o' us had been awa to Bastavoe for yoags for bait, and on the 28th wi' a fine quiet morning, frosty cold, it so happened that four boats were oot at the clack just at the back o' Turness and oot ower to the baas o' Wadderholm. And almost before we ran the bottom, we began to draw, nearly as fast as we could get the handlines doon (what think you?) large pretty ling! Ling, mind you, no haddocks or olicks, but large ling, rinning eight or nine to the hundredweight!

"The fish were taking like mad, and the fowerereens soon begood to be brawly deep in the water. Noo, although, as you ken, it was only a matter or twa of three miles to the pier, the men grudged the time it would take; for a chance like this wasna to be lost, the fish might stop taking ony minute. So to make more room, they gutted the fish on the spot, and in a moment, there surely wasna a maa frae the north end o' the isles to the sooth, that wasna on the spot. And after the maas came the boats frae aa roond, for the Muness and Easting and Colvadale men werena lang in jalousing when they saw the birds roond the boats, that fish were getting, and in a short time there were nearly a dozen boats aa fishing roond aboot a spot and within hailing distance o' ane anither.

"I've never seen a day's fishing like that either afore or since, for by the time that darkness came doon, and it's no lang coming in the month o' Janiwar, when aa the boats

were gathered at the pier in Oesund they had brough wi'
them fully a hundred hundredweight o' fine fish aa up to
the standard length.

"Wi' the helly coming in atween men thought that the
shoal, for it was naething less, would disappear, so you can
imagine they were oot early and anxious on Monanday
morning, boats frae baith east and wast. But the fish was
still there, even in the very mooth o' the Skuda, and to
make a lang story short, sae it gaed on for three whole
weeks, day after day o' fairly guid weather, wi boat after
boat coming to the pier wi' great fine ling, the water nearly
lippering the gunwales. Aye, aye, in a time o' sair distress
indeed, it was the beginning o' a new era for merchant and
folk alike.

"That was the greatest fishing o' ling I ever saw, but
generally, as I said afore, there was nae want o' fish nor o'
men to catch them. Man, I mind us using large pretty
turbot for linns to draw the boats up and doon ower.
There was nae market for them, or rather the market was
ower far awa, so aa man took what he wanted and threw
the rest aside. Yea, there was plenty o' fish and to spare
thenadays and mair than a hundred able fishermen here
aroond the Shore, and noo—there's dee and me going to the
pier to see if a Skerries' man has ony whitings or peerie
flukes to sell!"

"But about the *Harvest Rose*?" said I. It was my last
chance for another ten minutes would take us to the pier.

"Weel, the *Harvest Rose*, yes! She had missed stays,
through the strength o' the tide near the point, and had
gone broadside on the Fless, the rock that lies in the mooth
o' the Wick; she had swung round so that her bows were
tilted up and pointing into the wind. The mizzen mast had
snapped near the deck and was jabbling aboot in a tangle o'
gear to leeward. Her weather-side was canted high into the
air, and we could see her decks frae stem to starn, noo and
then, but generally you could see very little for the spune-

drift o' the seas breaking ower her. The crew by this time were aa safe ashore. They had got a line floated to the beach roond a barrel. By this means and wi' the help o' the men on the beach they had sent a thicker rope ashore, had hized their end o' it to the foremast heid, then climbed the mast and made their way to land doon ower it safe enough. Yea, they had got ashore safely but soaked to the hide, of coorse. Men had invited them to come to the hooses nearby, but they couldna tear themsels awa, and stood aroond in a clump together, watching their ship, puir sowls, hammering hersel to bits upon the skerry.

"Ane o' the crew was in a bad way; he was the cook, a black man, and when they aa had thought there was little chance for them, he had unbeknown broached the rum cask and filled himsel, so as to hae, as he said himsel afterwards, a good drink for the last time. He was so helpless by the time the ship strack, that in the end they couldna get him up the mast, whaur their safety line was rigged and they were sair puzzled how to get him ashore. At length they had tied the end o' a lang line aroond him, and the bosun had taen the ither end wi' him as he gaed down ower the rope frae the foremast. When the bosun reached the shore, the skipper and the mate who were the last to leave, lifted up the black man and threw him into the sea, and the men on shore, tagging on to the line, dragged him through the water, sometimes abune, sometimes no.

"By the time they got him ashore he was very deidlike. I saw him as he lay while men tried to revive him, and his face, I mind, was grey. I mind me thinking that a queer thing—a white man's face under the same experience would a been whiter than usual, why shouldna then a black man's face be blacker? But it wasna; it was as grey as the back o' a ling. He was carried under the shelter o' the muckle rock o' Heddiwick and the men wrocht wi' him and pressed him and birzed him this way and that way until maist o' the saat water and rum was oot o' him, and he begood to revive, and in a day's time (it was a week afore the crew had a chance o' getting awa) he was the cheeriest and liveliest ane among them.

"And I never saw such a vast and undumious sea, I think, in aa my lifetime. By this time it was flowing water, and wi' the airt noo mair southerly the tide was rinning in the face o' the wind and the Hardi was going mountains high wi' an awesome roar that could be heard abune aa thing, a roar sic as might a come oot o' the mooth o' the Pit itsel. The very air shook; even in the shelter o' a rock you had to shout in a man's lug afore he heard you.

"Wi' the tremendous force o' the seas and the flowing water, the side was driven oot o' her in a very short time, and the cargo begood to lift oot o' her. It was maistly paraffin in big widden casks, and as they smashed on the rocks the oil made the sea smooth atween ship and shore. But ootby the roaring tide lumps o' Blue Mull Sound were packing and pressing on the oily lume so that the waves were coming in lang heaving unbroken lines, and smashing in the face o' the banks and on the beach wi' a mass fearful to look at, and wi' sic a force that the solid rock under your feet shook wi' the dad o' it.

"Mair and mair casks smashed, and aye mair were bobbing aboot in the affrug; men would watch their chance and grab them as the wave receded, but even so they were soaked frae the croon and doon as they hauled them ashore; some still hale, some half fu, they were rowed up the beach and up-ended. Yea, there was plenty o' wrack wid too for she soon broke up, and every man was very busy until lang efter darkness came doon.

"But aboot the paraffin. As I was saying, maist o' the casks were broken and just had to be up-ended abune the beach, but that night, storm or no storm, and aa neist day and the neist, folk came wi' waterbuckets and milk pails and ulie kigs and widden says and what no, and carried paraffin for sowl and body. For months efterwards you couldna drink a cup o' tea but what you were aware o' paraffin, even the kirns had been filled so that for a lang time even the butter was paraffiny. As late as the neist simmer some had in their barns the very buoys o' the herring nets still hinging fu o' paraffin.

"In the lang o' the length the Customs men came nosing roond, but of coorse they fand naething but twartree broken empty casks. No but what some casks did get ashore hale (if you ever go aboot the banks a bit o' line is a fine thing to swap ower onything fleeting!) Ae man I kent had a fu cask hoided in his stack, but when he heard that the Customs men were searching through the very peats, he dang in the heid o' the cask, took the langest peats he could find, and dipped them in, ane by ane, until he had soaked up aa the paraffin. So he had what he caaed his lighting roog at the side o' the stack. He had mony a bright fire that winter but if onybody remarked aboot it he would say—yea, it had been a fine simmer for drying the peats!

"But here we are at the pier. Noo, noo, let us see if the Skerries' man has onything worth buying!"

GLOSSARY

aevir	giant
affrug	backwash of waves
almark	straying sheep
anyoch	enough
ayre	beach between waters
baas	hidden shoals or rocks
baed	dwelt
baess	cattle
bedral	bedridden person
benon	on top
birzed	compressed
bow, of meal	boll (140 lbs.)
bow, in general	buoy
brether	brothers
brook	enjoy
bruck	broken pieces
clack	inshore fishing grounds
coft	bought
craigs	fishing seat on rocks by shore
creepie	low stool
dad	thud
daek	stone wall
dee	objective case of du
dip dee a start	sit down a little while
doel and when!	woe and lamentation!
dowed	faded and soured
drysook	drought
du	you, familiar form
elbucks	elbows
fagareek	cigarette

it fairlies me	it will be a ferly or strange thing to me
fornenst	opposite
fowerereen	four-oared boat
gawpenfus	handfuls
gio	narrow rent in cliffs
gluff	sudden fright
grointed	grunted
haaf	deep sea fishing ground
hank	skein
Hardi	tide bore in Bluemull Sound
heth!	faith!
hoided	hid
hurl	wheelbarrow
humlit	without horns
inbiggit	self-centred
juppies	jersies
kishie	straw basket
leashed	lashed
leidfully	diligently
linn	to rest for a short time
looderhorn	horn used in foggy weather by fishermen
lornshune	shoes
lume	calm or oily patch
maa	seagull
moorikav	blinding snowstorm
narked	nagged
peenkled	peered and blinked
peerie	small
pluffed	emitted short puffs
purling	groping with fingers
raab	demolish
raabit	demolished
raaze	to grate the surface from
riving o' the dim	daybreak
rivlins	heelless shoes of skin
roog	heap
rooked	smoked
sained	blessed
sang	in phrase, be me sang! By my blood!

says	wash-tubs
scurm	shell
shakes (no great.)	of no great account
shot	after room of small boat
sixern	boat of six oars
spanged	jumped
steuch	thick cloud of dust, etc.
streen	the streen, yesterday evening
swap	hasty movement
trivil	grope
trows	trolls
true du me!	believe you me!
ulie kig	keg in which fish-livers were kept
undumious	tremendous
vill	strong pull at the oars
wap	throw
whilly	small boat
whitrit	weasel
yoag	cockle

6

"THE BEST LAID SCHEMES"

THE deep peace of summer night brooded over lonely Dalsetter with never a sound to break its silence but the occasional dry-weather call of the corncrake or the eerie drumming of a random snipe. To the west the moorclad slopes of Hevda were grey in twilight, and in the uncertain dreamy light of the brief northern night the lower heights to the south and east appeared almost to enclose as in a nest the trim and fertile fields and the straw-thatched steading that lay within their hollow ring. Scarcely two hours ago the sun had set and before another three had passed would rise again. Meanwhile all nature seemed to relax and rest, and man too seemed to have ceased from toil and worry to find forgetfulness in a brief repose. But had he?

Let us enter beneath the lowly roof of this lonely dwelling, remote from the haunts of men, and join the group that is seated at the long table in the living-room, a table whereon are indications of a recent meal. Surely here is an astonishing number of quiet elderly men, most of them grey-bearded, to be found seated together at midnight. The light is dim for no lamp has been lit, but we soon discern that they are met on some very weighty and serious business; there is a gloom about them altogether more than merely that of the waning light.

Thorburn Sigurdson, owner and master of Dalsetter, from his seat at the head of the table speaks quietly and impersonally as befits one who is revered as the wisest of men and the most skilled in all that pertains to the ancient laws of this Viking land.

"We have met here by mutual consent, at inconvenience to nearly all, and at risk to every one of us, to decide first of all whether we take any action, and if so what action in face of the great injustices under which this hapless island of Unst labours and is being crushed. You have individually sought my opinion and it I am prepared to give when I have heard each of you. Free speech is still ours though we must exercise it now in secrecy. Let each say what is in his heart and then we shall take counsel together."

There was silence for a little and then the figure on his right stirred, and there came rumbling the deep solemn voice of Saemund of Burrafirth. "I am older than any of you and so can speak first without apology. Every one of us was present a fortnight ago at the court held in Colvadale. Remember that court represented justice as seen by those who are now our rulers, God help us all—the Justiciary Circuit Court, whose findings are binding on us all, for you know as well as I do that at the Lawting now our own laws are disregarded, and our appeals not only ignored but regarded as indications of a treasonable spirit.

"You were at that court of justice and you know what happened. Every single charge was found proven, often through the evidence of ranselmen appointed by the Foud himself, often through the lying words of his own hired tools, and often through the ruthlessness of the law itself which holds a man guilty unless he can clearly prove his innocence. Hired spies are everywhere to twist harmless or careless words until they become deadly. So poor Marion is condemned to death for witchcraft because from her one cow she produces more butter than her neighbours from two; old Margaret of Cunnisgirt, driven by hunger and need, lays hold of one of her neighbour's sheep and loses everything she has, even her little patch of land. Olaf Manson finds himself accused of stealing a sheep from his own mother. The carcase is found in his barn by the ranselmen. He does not know how it came there, but he and his wife lose everything—goods, gear, and land. So it goes on, three or four more crofts forfeited, escheat as they call it, every circuit visit. Are we to do something or shall we continue to sit as we have done now for many years seeing our neighbours' lives and lands nibbled away, hoping every man that he will be the last to be swallowed? We are forbidden by our tyrants to leave the island, on pain of death, and forfeiture of lands of course. So as there is no help for us from outside the island, we must do what we can ourselves, and for my part I am resolved that we *must* act and am willing to bear a hand in any action we decide upon. I speak for Algar and Eyvind too, for as neighbours we have discussed the matter in the last fortnight as you advised us."

Thorburn turned to the bulky sombre figure on his left. "Is that right, Algar?"

Algar of Norwick agreed briefly. "We have been free men all our lives and we held that freedom as a thing as much our right as the sun and air of heaven. It is our right, and now, if we have to venture life for it, and fight, well, we can try that too! So I agree we must act, and the sooner the better."

Eyvind of Skaw took up the theme. "Though I live at the Back of Beyond, and though at the present rate it will take the ferry-loupers five or six years to reach me, after he had swallowed you all, I'm not willing to wait. It's lonely enough, as it is," he added whimsically, "it would be still lonelier without you all. Count on me in whatever you decide."

Thorburn looked towards the end of the table where together sat two large and handsome young men, Hakki of Dikkerem, hair and beard black and massive, vast shoulders and stout arms, his great hands resting on one another on the table before him. Rolf, Thorburn's own orphan nephew, reared in his own house and treated as a son, would have drawn attention anywhere. Nicknamed Raudi by reason of his magnificent red hair and beard he looked like a

romantic figure of Saga days even as he sat fidgeting and
turning his head restlessly from speaker to speaker.

"What does the younger generation think?" asked Thorburn. "Hakki, will you tell us?"

Hakki had sat motionless as though uninterested in the
proceedings, but now raised his eyes, grey, deep set and
quiet, stood up out of respect for his elders, and with a
smile said: "Nay, don't ask me. Ask Rolf here. Where he
leads I generally follow, and where we lead I think I can
promise few of the young men will hold back." He sat
down.

"Well, Rolf?"

Rolf jumped to his feet and while the two young men had
seemed equally large when seated you only now became
aware of his height as well as breadth. With his great
frame and the lively movements of his arms, his habit of
smashing his clenched fist into his open palm, or banging
it on the table, he seemed urgent to inspire his audience
with some of his own terrific energy. His speech cannot be
rendered into polite language, for in invective the Norse
tongue was as devastating as the axe of a Berserk in battle,
nor is there any point to be gained in stirring up the ashes
of a hatred of three hundred and fifty years ago. The gist
of it was that only when the men of Unst showed themselves utterly reckless in their daring would the tyranny of
these misbegotten sons of an appalling heredity be checked.
They were not men but wolves and worse. The maw of the
wolf could be satiated, the mean greed of these men could
not be, men who would skin a louse for its fat.

They had falsified weights and measures to their own
advantage; finding this gainful they had still further falsified them; they had ignored the ancient laws of the lands,
imposing their own as they wished, and interpreting even
those as it suited them. On lying charges they convicted
whom they would; often a man's life was forfeited, and
always his land. They had established their strongholds of

stone, building them with forced labour and extortion. On this poor isle of Unst the burden had been doubly heavy—not only had they had to contribute money, provisions, and their quota of men to the building of the archdevil Stewart's tower in Scalloway, but on them had fallen the full burden of the building of a castle on their own little island for one who aped his superior in rank, and his equal in baseness and wickedness. Finally to prevent any appeal for justice to the king, the only man who, by treaty between Denmark and Scotland, had the right to rule over them, they had declared it a capital crime (with confiscation of land, of course!) for anyone to leave the country without their permission.

Very well, let it be so! He was resolved that with the aid of all men in the island who were yet men and not tame dumb driven beasts, he would so act that all those foreign thieves who had come to the island should have their fill of land rammed down their dead gullets before they themselves were thrust into a hole in the ground, or thrown over the cliffs (why spoil good land?). And if in the accomplishment of this some of their own folk had to die, what of it? Was that such a dreadful thing? Was it not better for those whose fathers were free, and whose forebears had been Vikings, to die, gripping with their teeth if need be, their enemies' throats, than to drag out a haunted existence like base thralls and utter dastards.

As he stood thundering, his red beard out-thrust, he seemed like Thor himself in all his ruddy splendour, and his hearers were visibly stirred by his words, but Thorburn interrupted.

"Let the first point be settled first, Rolf. Am I right in thinking that we are all agreed that we must act, and act quickly?"

Rolf at his words had sat down quietly enough, but his scowl was still fierce. Nor did it pass when one and all agreed that action must be taken.

"I too agree," resumed Thorburn, "and have but this to say at the moment. Let us discuss our action without anger, calmly and without haste. Now has any man a definite plan?"

There was silence for a short time before Rolf rose again.

"Forgive me, Uncle, and you, my elders," he began more quietly, "but I did wait to see if any wished to take the lead before me. I have a plan and it will take no long time to lay it before you. The position of affairs you know. Bruce has under his control in the island between thirty and forty able-bodied tough soldier men more or less armed. At any given time the bulk of these are in the castle or in its vicinity, but there is a constant watch kept by a patro, along the east coast from north of Baltasound to Munessl and there is at the Westing and along that coast a like patrol. These maintain watch day and night but at times the watch is but slackly kept. Now during the last fortnight I have not been idle, and there are now more than forty young strong men who are willing to follow my lead. Both the patrols can be destroyed the same night—we have sufficient axes and harpoons still in spite of all their searching. Then if a party from the castle comes out in search of them it can be ambushed and cut off too, and with the weapons taken from our foes, we shall be strong enough to destroy the remainder of his force either in fight or by starving them out. We may even be able to enter the castle by a trick, wearing the dress and equipment of the slain patrols, before the inmates know what is happening.

"Either way, be it long or short, we shall make a clean sweep of them all, and leave of Bruce's castle not one stone upon another. The thing can be done, I do assure you, and Hakki here and I will see it through."

Algar spoke: "Suppose it were done, and it could be, what of the women and children and all the servant rabble within the castle? What of the vengeance that would

surely follow? Now we are ground to the dust by individual tyrants, then we would surely be utterly destroyed
by the armed might of Scotland."

"Possibly we would if Scotland ever learned of the deed
and if after learning she took action. In that case we
would be no worse off than we are at present. If war comes,
with the captured arms and equipment, with our knowledge
of the hidden places in the cliffs and hills, with the aid of
our winter storms and tempest-maddened seas we could
break the patience and the hearts of any force they send
against us. But need Scotland know? Only if information
is afforded her. And there will be no information given.
Every one of the hated brood, man, woman and child,
must be destroyed, and every inhabitant of the isle shall
be bound by oath, and by dread of what shall happen to
him both in this world and the next, not to disclose the
slightest information."

There was silence unbroken for quite a long time; then
Eyvind of Skaw, a man who usually saw something at
which to laugh, so much so that his neighbours declared
he would laugh at his own skin drying on a dyke, spoke
briefly and with great gravity.

"I say no to such a plan. It would succeed at first, but
it would be the beginning of a war of extermination, and
we men who could fight and die in battle would fare well
enough compared with the harrying and sufferings of the
old, the feeble, the women and the helpless children left
with none to protect them. And we would be fighting too
with the dreadful feeling that we had, after all our sufferings, put ourselves in the wrong with God and man. I said
before that you could count on me in whatever you decide
but I withdraw that. I will not have a hand in this whole-
sale massacre of the helpless. Against armed men I am
with you but all the others must be spared."

The discussion that followed was remarkably quiet.
Rising anger was ever promptly checked at a word from

M

Thorburn, and Rolf normally most unrestrained of all was content for a time to say no more.

But Saemund of Burrafirth, who had said little, at last entered the lists. He said that in this matter he agreed with Eyvind, but that before deciding even on limited warfare they should consider if there was no other way. When the islands were handed over to Scotland as the pledge for the payment of a Danish princess's dowry more than a hundred years ago, it had been regarded as a temporary matter, and on two conditions agreed to by both countries, that the islanders should retain their own laws and customs and be subject to none but the king and his legitimate heirs. These conditions had been violated, whether with the consent of the king or not they knew not. They could only find out by seeing the king in person as their forebears had done when they had a grievance in the old land of Norway. The penalty of death and loss of lands for leaving the island without permission he was willing to risk and would make one of the number to go.

Soon the meeting agreed to his proposal, Thorburn supporting him vigorously. It was their correct legal line of action and access to the king could even be bought if necessary, though he did not think it would be. Their oppressors, both Stewart of Scalloway and Bruce of Muness, had their enemies as well as friends at court, the Sinclairs of Caithness, the Earl of Morton and doubtless many others. He suggested (with an eye to continued peace in his absence) that both Rolf and Hakki accompany them. They would take sufficient money, too, to buy arms with in the event of their mission failing. Thus they would be in better shape for open war and in that case he, too, would support Rolf in his campaign but only as far as Eyvind and Saemund did. For a boat they would take his own sixern from Widwick and for crew what better men could he have than the men sitting round the table there? With favourable weather they could be at Leith in a week or ten days, and, with

God's help, back in their own homes in a month or so, even if they had to wait the king's pleasure for a fortnight.

One and all agreed to sail the day after next, each man taking what money he could, and provisions for ten days. After some further discussion and suggestions about the voyage itself the conclave ended and Thorburn rose, went to the door and called out "Helga!"

A young woman entered bearing a tray and glasses which she placed on the table before her father, who proceeded to fill them from a stone jar taken from the quaintly carved oaken sideboard convenient to his hand. The eyes of the elder men may have been on him as he did so but those of Hakki and Rolf were on her who had entered; Hakki's eye expressed interest and admiration, but Rolf, with all the fierceness of his Viking blood abated, gazed at her with a dog's eyes of devotion.

Helga, Thorburn's daughter was worth looking at in all the quiet charm of her young womanhood. Of medium height, twenty-three years old, dark-haired, with large brown kindly steady eyes, slim, neat and alert, she seemed so wholesome and good that one felt the better even for looking at her. She had, too, a gentle gravity and poise of manner beyond her years, as befitted one on whom the responsibility for the management of the household affairs had rested now for seven years, ever since her mother's death. The isolation of Thorburn's land in the hollow of the hills, the daily routine of farm and household work, the fact that she was an only child had developed her along unusual lines. To the eyes of her elders she seemed at first glance a staid, capable housewife, practical, kind and resolute, until one suddenly noticed that she was only a bonny girl with rather quiet manners. To younger men she was even more bewildering—she possessed all a girl's outward charms with little of the ways they generally associated with girls.

Nor was this to be wondered at. Throughout all her

childhood and youth she had known but one constant companion, her cousin Rolf, three years her senior. In strength, speed, and daring he excelled all others, and, impatient with everyone else, he had always been patient with her, and she, as fearless as himself, had shared with him many an adventure in cliff climbing, boating and fishing. She admired him as her big brother, feeling as kindly towards him as to her own father—only of late a shadow had fallen between them; she no longer understood him and sometimes felt uncomfortable and even slightly afraid in his presence.

After a parting drink the company dispersed and two nights later met as agreed at the lonely beach of Widwick. There was a slight haze over the western sea, growing denser towards the horizon behind which the sun had dipped an hour ago. Soon Helga stood alone on the rocky shore on which the long rollers dashed and spent themselves. The sea was almost calm, but there was a heavy lift and swell, and a chill seemed to fall on her spirit as the little boat quietly propelled by six oars entered into the mist wreaths and finally vanished in the long white pall that lay like a cold winding sheet on the face of the deep. They were gone—it was death for them if they were caught; and if they escaped, four hundred weary miles of sea to cross and cross again. A lonely gull wailed overhead. Helga shivered as she turned away. Some folk said gulls were the souls of dead seamen. What a pity she had thought about winding sheets, though that was all nonsense! There they were though she could not see them, each man pulling as quietly and calmly as though they had gone a-fishing, each with his own little box of gear and possessions under his legs at his own side of the thwart, the fire in its kettle with the peats around, the food and water aft under the kanni, a few fishing lines, too, in the foreroom. The boat and all its gear were tested and good, and the crew, every man of them tried seamen. They would be away only five weeks or so, and times would surely be happier when they returned. She turned and resolutely climbed the steep winding valley. Stopping at a turn in the track from which she could obtain a last glimpse of the sea she looked back. Where the gap in the cliffs should have revealed the sea, she saw only the cold white pall of mist.

II

As he stood before his castle in the sunlight of a lovely August morning, Laurence Bruce, late of Cultmalindie in Perthshire and now Great Foud of Shetland, and as such responsible for the administration of the law, glanced with a measure of pride at the inscription carved in stone above the main doorway. It looked well.

List ze to know this building quha began
Laurence the Bruce he was that worthy man
Quha earnestly his heiris and affspring prayis
To help and not to hurt this work always.
Zeir of our Lord 1598.

The castle was rawly new, but all castles had been raw and new at some time or other; the green slopes and the little loch in front were pleasant to the eye and conjured up a vague recollection of Linlithgow Palace. But only for an instant. Where were the trees? Trees had no chance in this climate. Oh, yes, at the moment the mirror of the little loch was ablaze in the sun's rays, not a ripple on its surface. To the eastward the great sea itself was smooth from the shore to the dim horizon where bright sea and bright sky melted into each other. The heavens seemed filled with the joyous song of the larks pouring out their strain in wild abandonment. Truly a fine morning! But such days were few in comparison with the number of wet and stormy days; the constant wet of winter that got into a man's bones, and the winds that could at any season roar for days like devils unleashed.

He turned in kindly fashion to his companion whose dandified garb and jaunty manner contrasted with his own rather rough homespun. "You mustn't think, Edwin, that we always have such weather as this. Na, Shetland weather and Shetland folk, too, are gey unchancy. You see yon black rock lying noo like a log by its lane oot on the face o' the sea with never a ripple round it; the seas may be spouting twenty feet high ower it before the morn; and ower there yon quiet waters may be boiling ower rocks and reefs mair dangerous still, reefs that never show their teeth, but lying near enough the surface to destroy in bad weather the best ship afloat. Ye'll find the Shetlanders just the same, smiling at ye to your face, but underneath the surface hating ye like hell. No but that they have been quieter of late; they begin to learn their lesson. Twenty years ago they held their heads as high as ony Douglas or Lord o' the Isles ever did, speaking o' their rights to this and their rights to that, their laws, their customs, their land tenure and what no. Noo it's oor ain guid Scots law that rins here, and I see it rin! If they canna prove their rights by Scots law—weel, sae much the waur for them—and the better for us!

"Ye will find that since you were in Shetland last, five years ago, we now have a lot mair land—a' legally come by, but it takes time, it takes time, and I'll be glad o' your help noo. But first, laddie, ye maun hae a rest, just roam aboot and get some colour in your cheeks an flesh on your bones. Then I'm hoping wi' your scholarly lear, and your knowledge o' Latin and the law, ye may take some o' the burden off my shoulders."

In the five weeks which followed, Edwin the scholar who at first had devoted his time to brief walks, now to one district then to another, suddenly became Edwin the hunter. Armed sometimes with bow and arrow, sometimes with a musket and powderbag and shot, he frequently went out early for his hunting and returned late; seldom did he have aught to show for his efforts and endured with serenity all the chaff and scoffing at his lack of success. Nor did he heed his father's hints that it was time he helped him in his work. Finally, indeed, when he was being shown the records of the recent Circuit Court findings, with its list of forfeitures of patches of land, of animals, and gear, he had exclaimed: "How pitiful!" and had thrown the list from him with an air of contempt. It worried his father—there were some things in that same list which he regarded with some contentment. His eyes ran down the sheet in perplexity. "10 July 1602. Anent the accusation of Margaret Petersdochter, for the theftous steilling of an sheip of hir nighbors, having na sheip of her awin, comperit the said Margaret in judgment, and confest the stowth of the said sheip, not knowing quha aucht the samen, confessing the samen to be done in plain hunger and necessite; quhilk being considert be the Assise, and trying this to be the first fault, dicernis her haill guids, and gere, and landis, gif ony be, to be escheat, and hirself to be banist the countrye within the space of an monet at the least in the first passage; and gif she beis apprehendit with the walor of ane viristhift heirafter to be tane and drownit to the daith to the example of utheris.

"Anent the accusation of Olaw Mawnsoun, for the theftous steilling of ane sheip of his motheris, quhiek was ransellit, and found with him quha being accusit thairfoir in judgment, could not deny the samen; yet not the less the Assyse takand consideration thairinto, and finding the samen to be the first falt, decernis his and his wyffis haill guid and gere and landis to be escheat, and themselffs to be baneist the countrye within the space of an monet, at the leist in the first passage, and gif thai be apprehendit in the walor of an viristheft heiraftir, to be tane and put to the daithe, in exampill of utheris."

And so on and so on.

To the Great Foud of Shetland, the man responsible for the administration of the law within the isles it all seemed fair enough. People must be taught to observe the law, even if it inconvenienced them as it did himself. He himself was at great expense; for to maintain its majesty he had to find food, clothing, arms and shelter for a great rabble of old retainers and fighting men, without whose aid there would be no law, no central government at all. But when he had tried to explain to Edwin the obstinacy and treachery of the natives, how he had had to force them to contribute food, money, labour and material to the building of the castle, how he had had to prevent them from leaving the island by threat of death and forfeiture of everything they possessed, how his fighting men had to watch by day, and his ranselmen by night, Edwin had but looked at him and turned away. He seemed to be interested in nothing at home—content to roam the hills and return empty handed more often than not—even his hunting seemed to be feckless. Laurence, his father, was perplexed and disappointed.

But Edwin's hunting had been far from ineffective in one way at any rate. For a day or two he had hunted to the south, round the Gallow Hill, the wilds of Bordastubble, the Blue Mull and the Westing shore. Then feeling discontented and restless he had wandered farther afield, climbing dark Valafield over the shoulder of the steep Erne's Hamar, and wandering along its ridge past the hidden little tarn until he stood on Byre o' Scord the highest point of all and gazed out towards the west where the Atlantic Ocean and the North Wind had fretted the end of the adjacent isle of Yell into pleasant sandy bays between dark frowning headlands, and where far on the horizon lay the black humps of the Ramna Stacks. Nearer, the majestic sweep of the south tide marked by eddies on the quiet waters of its margin swept by the Westing Holms and was pouring into narrow Blue Mull Sound between the isles.

Down below, so sheerly below the seven hundred feet of height on which he stood that it seemed he could throw a stone upon them, lay a few humble straw-thatched roofs, the dwellings of some poor devils he thought, who after generations and generations of wild undisciplined freedom from all restraint, were now being compelled to conform to the system and order imposed by Scotland's feudal laws, laws in themselves harsh and harshly interpreted. Over to the east, three miles away, the North Sea glittered, and to the south and east the massive pile of Muness Castle on its knoll caught the eyes even at this distance. To the north-west, a little hillock somewhat interrupted his view, and he went forward unknowingly—to fulfil his destiny.

When he had ascended the short easy slope he met with two surprises. He found himself close to a cliff which descended so steeply and so far to the sea that, though the swell was breaking white and gulls were wheeling far down, no sound reached him. And close beside the cliff's edge and within a few yards of him there sprang up from a stone a woman who glanced at him and began to hurry away.

Possibly had the glimpse he obtained of her face and the youthful ease of her movements intrigued him less, he would not have acted as he did but his own weird led him on. He hastened after her calling out to her not to be afraid and she turned and faced him boldly. Though Thorbjorn Treefoot and Auslag his daughter, the resolute rescuer of Goturm, had been ashes and dust for more than six hundred years, and though their very names were forgotten, some of their proud and fearless spirit yet lived in her.

He apologised briefly and sincerely for startling her, explained that he was hunting and had never been here before, and that he found the scenery so wonderful that he often rambled on forgetful of the chase. As she listened she

smiled slightly at his pronunciation of her Shetlandic
tongue, frowned as she recognised he must be one of the
hated Scots, and when he brought his words diffidently to
a close, she answered him politely and in distant manner
and turned away. He made no attempt to follow.

Helga, after refraining for three days from visiting her
favourite eyrie on the cliff top where she had been disturbed, persuaded herself that it would be cowardly to
refrain simply because she might there meet the Scots
stranger again; such a thing was unlikely. Edwin, who for
three days had tried to forget the most beautiful and wholesome creature he had met in all this savage isle, and had
avoided Valafield accordingly, on the fourth day decided to
try to shoot a skua on that hill. So far he had not encountered one of these rare birds except on Valafield.

So they met again, and yet again. Though her father
could not possibly return for several weeks yet, Helga,
whenever the weather was fair, had to ascend the height to
look for his sail; though no skua had as yet fallen to Edwin's
bow or musket, there remained always the chance of getting
one whenever the weather was fair. She was lonely and
found him attractive; he was lonely whenever he was from
her side. It is useless to ask why he who had been on
friendly terms with some of the fairest daughters of Scotland's capital should have succumbed so absolutely to this
island maiden, no use asking why she, who had been accustomed to hard work among a strong race of men and women
who all had to labour strenuously, should give her heart to
this gentle rather helpless person of an alien and hated race.
There it was; the fact remains that for them both the next
few weeks were very happy, culminating in a mutual
declaration of their abiding love for each other. Their
moment of happiness was short.

Hitherto they had known each other merely as Helga and
Edwin, but now the latter diffidently, as one who feared the
effects of his words, said:

"I must tell you, Helga, my name is Edwin Bruce. I am a son of Laurence Bruce of the Castle."

He watched in horror her face grow pale, and hurried on nervously before she could speak.

"Oh, I know your people hate him, and indeed, though he is my father, I admit he has done harsh things, but you and I have a chance of composing all feuds and animosities between our people. Take me to your father to-day and I will ask him for you in marriage."

But Helga cried out as though in pain. At this moment her father and his best friends and Rolf her cousin were staking their lives to check the wicked tyrant who for long years had compelled free men to go in fear and servitude, and here she was listening to that tyrant's son and (God help her!) loving him! What could she do? What could she do?

"Please, Helga, let me come and see your father. Everything will be all right." When she made no reply he continued his urging for some time. But Helga needed time to be alone and think, and they parted agreeing to meet in two days' time.

She made up her mind in that time. When her father returned she would tell him all and abide by his decision. If he brought back good news, if his pleading of the islanders' cause had been successful, if justice was to prevail and restraint had been placed on the tyrant, her father might consent; indeed, he probably would. But if they had failed then she was sure her father would be averse to such a union, and she herself would in that case rather abide in unhappiness with her own people, than in a position even of the highest honour among the oppressors. So she decided and when next they met she made excuses. As she was resolved that through her no mention should be made of her father's absence, not even to Edwin, she merely said that it would be better to wait for some days before approaching her father; only let him have patience and perhaps all would be well.

III

It was now early in September and the long spell of fine
weather began to show signs of breaking as was to be
expected with the approach of the equinox. Over the hills
in Muness one sunny gusty morning Laurence Bruce (the
Bruce as he liked to term himself) sat moodily in his own
sanctum, a room high in the south-west corner of the castle
facing across four miles of sea the towering cliffs of Fetlar's
East Neap—blue in the distance. What was it that old
trickster Macgregor used to say in Perthshire lang syne?
"Aye, aye, blue are the hills that are far awa!" By G—,
there was some truth in that too! Everything in the far
distance, hills and cliffs, and plans—aye, even a man's own
life, seemed bright and pleasant, until one came to nearer
grips with them. Here he had been in this godforsaken
land now for more than thirty years, and he had never had
a moment's rest, aye, striving more than anyone around
him, and it was slow work, slow work!

That boy Edwin might have been such a help with his
quick mind and his lear, and he had had great hopes in
him, for as for Alexander and Andrew they were what they
were—just lumps, generally able to see as far as their nose
but no much further. But Edwin seemed to care for nothing
but aimless roaming. Well, he smiled grimly to himself he
would give him something to care for! He would find him a
wife, with a bit of land, of course. That would clip his wings
for him, and even if it did not, the land would aye be there.

He rose to his feet and crossing the room studied with
care a rough map of the island hanging on the wall. Already
it showed a considerable portion scored with the red lines
of possession, but the unscored portion was yet vexingly
larger. His left hand tugging at his beard he gave the
matter serious consideration.

But he was interrupted. There was a discreet knock at
the door and Robert Kennedy most efficient of all his

ranselmen entered. He spoke as he lived, cringingly and furtively. "I hae something important to tell ye, sir, at least I think ye'll say it's important when ye hear it." Bruce knew his man and asked him to be seated, and soon he too glumly admitted the importance of the tidings.

It proved that Robert, in the execution of his duty, had had occasion to lie on the straw-thatched roof of Virse, a croft house some few miles away, in the darkness listening to the conversation of the inhabitants to pick up scraps of information which might prove useful. (By the way, the memory of such like activities on the part of Robert and his colleagues has been preserved in a very quaint saying. Instead of using the phrase about little pitchers having long ears as a caution when we do not wish some child or stranger to obtain inconvenient information the old Shetlander may still say: "The roof draps soot." In former times with the fire in the middle of the floor, the rafters and roof were naturally sooty, and if soot dropped it could be an indication that someone was listening on the roof outside. So "the roof draps soot" means "take care, others are listening.) Not to diminish his own share in this important matter, Robert told his tale at some length, but the gist of it was this. Someone had drunk a toast to the "return of the boat", and by giving careful attention and at considerable risk he had learned that a party of six men led by Thorburn of Dalsetter, a man the natives regarded as a wise lawman and an able speaker, had set out nearly six weeks ago to lay complaint at the king's court about the oppression of Bruce and his open violation of the islanders' rights.

"Aye," he added, not without malice, "and yin o' them said wi' a laugh that he hoped the auld bastard wad get his kail through the reek this time."

"Did he so?" said Bruce. "But that can wait! Have you learned if they were speaking truth? Has a boat left the island?"

"Yes, there's no doubt at all about it, though I learned only Thorburn's name and that of his nephew Rolf. The auld man it appears has the gift o' the gab, and the young man is held to be the best seaman in the isles. So they're sure that they would get through to Scotland, and fairly sure they would get a hearing."

"Well, well, what's done canna be undone! Sax weeks ago you say; they may be back any day now. What about this Thorburn of Dalsetter?" He learned as much as Robert knew about Dalsetter and its inhabitants and dismissed him briefly with thanks.

Bruce could act quickly. He sent word to his men on watch to keep a sharper lookout for a boat coming from the south and to arrest its crew. Now what else? It appeared this Thorburn's family consisted of but one daughter. He would seize her as a hostage to stop his mouth, if indeed he had had any success in Edinburgh—if he had not, so much the better! Aye, the very thing, (he smiled to himself), he had been thinking just now how to cure the loon Edwin of his rambling ways, well, here was a wife for him! Dalsetter was not a large estate but it would pass to the daughter; if she wasn't worth having that would be Edwin's worry, the land would aye be there! He would get Willie Lauder to join them in lawful wedlock, and Thorburn's face would be worth seeing when he got the news!

He immediately sent a party of three men on ponies and taking a spare mount with them to Dalsetter.

"Tell Thorburn o' Dalsetter's daughter that her father and Rolf are here at the castle with their men, and that her father wishes to have speech with her. Ye can hint that he's hurt—aye, say he's no sair hurt but say it in such a way that she'll believe he is; say ye hae brocht a pony in case she wishes to come. If as I expect she comes willingly—good, but if no tak her wi as little ado as need be."

Life is full of ifs. If the fine weather of the last six weeks had but continued fine for only another six hours all might have been well, and the story could have ended very differently. But as the morning passed the wind strengthened from the north-east. By the time Bruce's men had reached Dalsetter the sun had disappeared, swallowed up in a massive mantle of menacing cloud, and the breeze was blowing in strong gusts.

There was no difficulty in finding Helga for she herself came to meet them, and on learning of their tidings did not hesitate for an instant. She ignored the advice of Ivar, on whose shoulders Thorburn, on his departure, had laid the responsibility of her safety. He suggested that he himself should go first to find out if the tale were true: Muness Castle was no place for an unprotected lass to go to. But Helga's mind was full of the thought of her father lying there hurt; and Edwin would be there; no harm could befall her beside him. She bade the men wait a few minutes while she made ready for the journey and ordered Ivar to bring them refreshment.

No time was lost and the little party of four rode over the hills in silence, for the men themselves were taciturn, and Helga's mind was occupied fully with her own thoughts. In any case the wind now blowing almost a full gale would have prevented conversation.

It was late afternoon by the time they reached the castle and Helga was received somewhat stiffly by a lady of imposing manner, considerably older than herself, and whom the leader of the escort addressed as Lady Marjory.

"Come this way, my father is expecting you," and she led the way up a cold stone stairway and through the wide banquet hall.

"Stop for a moment, please," cried Helga. "How is my father now?"

"*Your* father?" stammered the lady, and she did stop in astonishment. "I don't know what——" she checked herself and said no more but moved on. This was likely one more of her father's subtle tricks—anyway, it was no business of hers. He had simply told her to bring the young woman to him and she was doing so. They passed on into a room at the far end of the hall, and there by a window looking out on the now storm-tossed waves beyond the Ness, sat Bruce.

He rose as she entered. "Come awa in, lassie! So ye're Helga, Thorburn's dochter, are ye?"

"Yes, I am Helga. Where is my father?"

"Your father, honest man, if what I hear be true, is awa on some fule errand to Edinburry making trouble on his betters. He wad hae been better employed, I'm thinking if he had stayed at hame looking after his bit lass. But dinna worry, I'll look efter you, and when he does return he'll find maybe what he could a found by remaining at hame, namely that I mak a better friend nor an enemy. At least if no a friend I'll be a kind o' relative onyway."

"I don't know what you mean," faltered Helga. For the first time in her life she was in the presence of something she recognised as both ruthless and malevolent.

"Sit doon, lass, sit doon. What I'm going to tell you will surprise you a bit maybe but you'll get ower it. I hae brocht you here for your wedding, and troth, you'll mak a bonnie bride the morn. Oh, ye shall be weel married; to ane o' my ain sons, nae less, and the knot shall be tied by an ordained minister at that, Willie Lauder. He haes a' his preceptor's ideas aboot women, mind ye, and Knox had little time for them, in the poopit at onyrate. So if ye think o' greeting or making ony steer you can hain your trouble wi' him, and if the groom I pick for you is no to your liking, by God, I'll marry you to yin o' the hinds."

Helga had leaped to her feet at the word wedding, and as he continued she listened as if in a dream. She had been tricked; it could not be possible though that she, petted from infancy and held in respect and love by all she met could be so addressed. Her face flushed and anger burned within her but the sneering voice went on:

"And now as I'm a busy man ye'll hae to excuse me. I maun send you to your room where to-day you'll have good food and every comfort, and then to-morrow aboot noon a braw bridegroom a' to yersel."

Without more words he went to the door and cried: "Marjory!" and his daughter entered immediately.

"Tak this lass to the guest-room upstairs. See that she has a good meal and everything she needs, but see the door is kept locked. If she makes trouble get what help you need."

Marjory beckoned to her without a sign of emotion. Helga looked from her to Bruce and suddenly her rage passed. She felt herself swept along as in a vast tideway in whose current she was powerless. It must carry her whither it would; it was bearing them all along and Bruce too was but a straw upon it. She said quietly: "Why I say what I say I know not, but you will remember this weary day with sorrow for evermore!"

He was taken aback, and before he could reply she left the room following her guide.

The room was lofty and spacious, well furnished, and with a cheerful peat fire blazing on its wide hearth. Its window, with the wooden shutters (there was no glass) partly closed against the strong gusts now roaring with increasing violence, looked out to the south and east over the now raging stretch of sea between the Ness and Fetlar. Midway, and partly hidden in sheets of driving spray and the white foam of the great breaking rollers, lay the green islet of Haaf Gruney. Within the room an ample meal was set on a large square table, a huge four-poster bed stood in the corner beside the window. The capacious armchairs, the bright silver candlesticks, winking in the light of the peat fire, the dyed wool rugs all spoke of comfort. But they could not make her forget the grating of the lock as the key had turned to shut her in. She had always been free to come and go as she would, locks and bars were to her

N

things unknown, and now she was a prisoner in the hands of a callous, treacherous liar, apparently without pity. She sat down by the fire and after a few minutes found some relief in tears.

She soon recovered. Tears would help her but little. She must escape somehow and was resolved to do so. Not even if Edwin should prove to be the husband promised would she wed on such terms. But it was by no means certain, hardly even likely that Edwin was the son referred to. But not even to him would she be married in this fashion without her father's consent and to the thwarting of his efforts for freedom. And while she remained a prisoner here his hands would be tied and his mouth stopped.

She went to the window and leaning out looked down. The ground was perhaps fifty feet away. It seemed a long distance down but she did not quail at the thought of descent if only she had a rope. She looked round the room then turned to the bed and, to her satisfaction, found that she had the material at any rate for the making of a kind of rope. But she must wait until night. With but a glance at the table and its food, she returned and looked out to sea, to judge how long it would be before darkness fell. And then she gasped.

Far away, close by the point of distant Strandabroch, was a little dark speck tossing, now in sight now lost to view, among the waves. To all other eyes in Muness that speck might betoken just a little boat battling courageously in the storm, but Helga had watched that sail too often to be mistaken. It was the *Otter* and her father at last! They were returning and that in itself she regarded—she knew as a token of success.

For a time she continued to gaze. There were moments when she stared anxiously at the spot where it had disappeared in the turmoil of breaking seas but ever it bobbed up again a little farther on its course. She knew she need not worry, the men who had held their little craft safely on its path for so many hundred miles would not be beaten now in sight of home; with Rolf at the helm and her father at the sail they would be safe. In thought she was far from the castle in the boat helping to bail and watching the lumpy seas ahead. But as she continued to look she began to realise that there was danger for them not from the sea but from the land. With the wind now more from the north they would never get round the north of Unst in this weather—the strings of Skaw would be impossible—they would have to land in the territory of Bruce and his men, somewhere south even of Baltasound. Gradually the sail crept northward but nearer now to Unst and when the angle of the castle walls at last shut them off from her view she began again to think of her own plight.

The door was locked from without so there was no egress that way; she would make entrance difficult too. With some effort she slowly moved the heaviest piece of furniture, a large oaken wardrobe, and placed it against the door, backing it up with the table and the two large chairs. Then she proceeded to cut and tear the sheets and blankets from the bed into substantial strips and to knot them together. Though she must wait until darkness for her attempt at descent she would avail herself of the remaining daylight for her preparation. Time went past and she was engrossed in her work when a sudden shouting and outcry from the ground drew her again to the window.

She was just in time to see a large party of men disappear round the corner, and she guessed that the boat had been seen and that these men had hurried away to intercept the crew when they landed. She conjectured aright, for already about a dozen men armed with pikes and muskets and under the leadership of Bruce himself had set out to arrest them.

So strongly now blew the gale that the party plodded against it with bowed heads over the Brake of Voesgrind

and down to the long stretch of the white sands of Sandwick, at the south end of which were arising the half-built
walls of a large new house—to be Bruce's gift to his
daughter Marjory on her approaching marriage. But they
passed it without a glance. When a head was raised it was
to look at the little boat seething along in a white yeast of
foam, the very tip of its dauntless sail often disappearing
amid the surge of spume-capped waves. It was considerably to leeward of the Vair, on which the waves were
spouting to the sky in a welter of greeny white torment,
and judging by its course it would gain the north end of
the sands to the southward of the chapel. Laurence
shouted to his men to hasten and halted them at the north
end of the sands. The boat approached swiftly.

Aside to Robert Kennedy, Bruce imparted his instructions.

"They must be very exhausted, and it's not likely they
will resist, but if they offer to, you, Robert, will shoot down
the first man of them that moves. That will put an end to
all obstinacy on their part."

To the others he cried: "You will arrest these men when
they land. They may be pirates or holm-raiding sheep-
thieves for all we know," and he grinned to himself. "Stand
ready all!"

The men drew up roughly in line along the verge of the
sands, but of a sudden the boat, when almost within musket
range, nosed up into the wind, down came the sail, and in
an instant went up again while the boat heeled over on the
other tack to seaward. The men swore among themselves.

"They're trying to get north to the shelter of the Broch.
With this airt they may be able to beach her there." It
was Robert Kennedy who spoke. "We'll need to hurry if
we mean to catch them."

Hurry they did along the rocky coast, the spray from its
jagged cliffs and howling reefs stinging their faces as they
moved; past Sandwick churchyard with its quiet dead;

past the point of Quiness where the very air seemed to shake with the all pervading thought-obliterating roar of the vast seas upon its pounded rocks. Twice, in spite of their hurry, they stopped. "She's gone!" The sail had disappeared. But no! Up it came again! Past the Gio of Meal, past the burn of Colvadale, and at last after plodding nearly two miles they reached the Broch noosts and, crouching under the lee of a low stone wall, waited for the boat again rushing landward.

"They must land here," said Robbie. "Neither man nor devil could noo gain Baltasound in the face o' this wind and the tide coming round Huney. Well, they know it, trust them, they must land here."

"Deevils they may be," said Bruce, "but, by my soul, they can sail a boat. Aweel, we a' hae oor gifts."

At a motion of his hand his men wearily arose and moved down over the rough stony beach to meet them.

Once more they were for the moment foiled. Within a hundred yards of the shore, again the sail was lowered, but this time the boat turned southward; the sail was up in an instant and if the boat had raced before now she seemed to fly over the waters with the roaring wind behind her. The massive figure at the helm turned for an instant and waved his hand in derision, and Bruce's temper for a moment broke loose. On his orders a volley was fired, ragged and without effect, except for another mocking gesture from the red-headed giant who was steering. Robert had quietly refrained from shooting—nae use wasting good pooder on impossible shots. "They mean to land at the sands after all," quoth he. "They'll be there nearly half an hour before us now."

Bruce urged his reluctant followers southward, wet with the spray and weary, and even against their wills feeling something of admiration and pity for the supreme skill and more than human tenacity with which these poor devils, who must be now utterly exhausted, had kept their drenched and drowned little craft above the surface in such a stupendous uproar of the elements. Scarcely could men fresh and vigorous have launched a boat and kept her afloat during the short two or three hours they had seen her, but that these men, after a sea voyage of more than three hundred miles, should have been able to do so—it was unnatural, it was witchcraft! Speeding as though on wings it swiftly outdistanced them in spite of all their leader's urging. When in the end they passed the little chapel again and reached the place by the low cliffs where the hard rock gives way to sand, there safely propped and snug in a little hollow twenty feet above high water mark stood the boat and men were yet moving round about it. Bruce forgot his weariness in a feeling of exultation. So, here was the end of the pursuit; he had them all now safely in the bag at last!

IV

As they drew nearer, instead of hastening, they involuntarily slackened pace, for what was this that met their eyes? Small wonder they were perplexed at first—the boat seemed to have spewed forth men. Instead of six poor dripping wretches so enfeebled that they could hardly stand there was a concourse of fifty men at least, all shouting, gesticulating, laughing gustily, and slapping each other on the back!

As Bruce's party slowly approached as though mesmerised, man after man among them gradually realised what had happened. All throughout Unst for the last two weeks thoughts had been centred on and eyes had searched the waters for, the return of the boat on which all their hopes were fixed. Little else had been spoken of privately among them during that time. Scores of men in the then populous districts of Sandwick and Colvadale had scarcely been able to take their eyes from it ever since it appeared.

Seamen themselves, they shared in thought every movement and moment of the peril and discomforts, even swaying and twisting their bodies in the intensity of their
sympathy with the men on board. When the party from
the castle with evident hostile intent had passed along the
coast they, too, had been seen and cursed of all. For a long
time the boat's battle with the heavy seas south of Huney
had immobilised them all—if she won through to Baltasound the men would possibly be safe from Bruce's clutches,
but it was impossible that any boat could live to win the
shelter of the sound. When she turned at last and sped for
the sands outdistancing her enemies then man after man
realised he, too, must do something. They seized food and
drink and any weapon to hand, spade, pitchfork, whaling
lance, or reaping hook and hurried down from Hannigart,
Gairdaboiten, Still, Framgord, Hoosigart, Hooligart, and
Smirgart to meet the boat and its crew. These men needed
food and help; they brought news, if good so much the
better, if bad, well, they would all share in their fortune;
but come what may Bruce should not have them!

So here they all were near the boat facing Bruce and
actually laughing at him, for the news was good and had
been swiftly imparted to them. He on his part moved
forward to within a short distance of them, his men beside
him, and cried out harshly for he was both weary and angry.
"Let all the boat's crew, leader and men, come forward and
give themselves up as the pirates, sheep thieves or rebels
they probably are. They shall have food and safe accommodation, I'll see to that, and a fair trial and justice, for
I'll see to that, too. The rest of you get to your kennels
before worse happens to you!"

His answer was a roar of laughter from which he shrank
more than from a blow. The armour of power, however
ponderous, is utterly vulnerable to laughter—even Alexander the Mighty killed his best friend for laughing at him.
Even while he glared with an uneasy unfamiliar feeling that

he was not master of the situation, a thick-set bearded oilskin clad figure came forward a little from the mass of men in front of the boat, closely followed by the huge red-bearded devil who had mocked him at the Broch.

"Laurence Bruce," the words came in full deep-throated tones with only the slightest hint of exultation, "hear what these men——" and he swept his arms to right and left to indicate the now silent crowd behind him—"what these men have already learned. Your king and ours—God bless him—declares that he is sending north as soon as maybe a royal commission to inquire into the state of our islands here, and that in the meantime no man shall forbid or hinder his subjects to come or go where they will; and that we his island subjects shall aye have as is our special right free access to his own ear at all times. So you or anyone else who tries to hinder us will have to answer for it to the king himself."

"Say ye so!" said Bruce, who had listened with great intentness and had somewhat regained possession of himself, "ye have been moving surely in very exalted places to daur tell me what the king says! How do I know you are speaking the truth? Ye seem to me mair likely a parcel o' rogues oot on a sheep stealing ploy and caught by the storm. So let's hae nae mair trouble wi' ye; gie yersels up and tak' your medicine."

"Not even such a pretence shall be left you," firmly retorted the seaman, "the pretence of not knowing who we are. We considered you would so act and took the precaution of obtaining two copies of the royal command. The one is for ourselves, so that through it all men may see the king's will; the other is for you. You, who are doubtless accustomed to the very exalted places you mention, will recognise the royal signature and the royal seal."

Thorburn thrust his hand inside his oilskin coat, drew out a roll carefully wrapped and stepped boldly forward.

It is exasperating to think how the brief act of one stupid or bad man may plunge myriads of individuals for generations into a welter of misery, hatred, and destruction. God help us all! There's good in all men if one digs deep enough, but evil is ever more on the surface, swifter in action and more combustible. If it could burn away itself only, but ever it destroys with it so much that is fine and good! Here was a situation which if tactfully handled might have led to peace and even in time to a measure of mutual respect if not friendship. As things happened all that had to wait for hundreds of years.

As Thorburn stepped forward so boldly, Robert Kennedy, ever mindful of his orders and ever on the alert to curry favour with his master, raised his musket and fired. He was an accurate shot and the range was short. A dark ragged spot appeared on Thorburn's left breast—he swayed for a little time though it seemed long to those who gazed motionless with horror upon him, then fell on his face, the roll clenched in his hand. Almost before he touched the ground, Rolf had bounded forward with a roar like an enraged lion and thrust his whaling spear with such vehemence through Robert's breast that the gory blade protruded two feet behind his back. Setting his foot upon the fallen man he violently tore it out again and stood, an awful figure facing Bruce himself, ready and even eager it seemed to thrust again.

Had Bruce moved or cried out to his men it would certainly have been his last act, and as violence begets violence there would have ensued a massacre which would have stained the annals of the isle, for by this time the islanders' numbers had been greatly augmented by the men of Colvadale hastening to see what was happening, while Bruce's men receiving no instructions from their leader shuffled uncomfortably and merely waited. Nearly all of them had empty muskets, as they had been hurried on after their vain volley at the Broch. As it was the two men stood motionless glaring within five feet of each other. Hate there was in plenty between them but no fear. All eyes were on them and no man moved.

No man but one. From the west, between the two groups, came running one who shouted: "Stop, for God's sake, stop!" and Edwin spent with running, bare-headed and exhausted, came between them.

He had been absent all the day on some business of his father's at the south-west end of the isle, and on his return, before entering the castle, had heard of the boat's appearance and of the departure of his father with his men to intercept it. Pity of the islanders had never been absent from his heart, and Helga's love had given him sympathy with them too. He had hurried on, hoping to be of service to them, whoever they were, for Helga's sake, as he thought, though he had no knowledge that Helga was so closely concerned with them. When still some distance away he had heard the shot and had seen what followed. Now he stood almost between them and his slight dishevelled figure seemed to the eyes of all insignificant when compared with the two massive antagonists who still held the centre of the stage, their eyes fixed on each other.

But his words were so far from insignificant that they penetrated even to Rolf's maddened brain.

"For God's sake, men, stop, and see what you are doing, what you have already done! Murder is a fearful thing in which to have the least share, as you will find when the rope is around your neck, if you do not heed my words. Cease this mad strife which has already cost two lives! What I say, I say to both parties; the first man among you, though he were my own father, who moves to break the king's peace will have to reckon with my witness against him before the king himself."

There was silence for a little, for his declaration had taken both parties by surprise. Then someone from the mass of the islanders cried out:

"Ask your ain father how *he* received the king's word, still lying yonder in a dead man's hand." There was a shout of approval from their ranks and one or two voices added: "Aye, ask him that."

Edwin looked towards dead Thorburn, hesitated and then went forward and took the roll from the stiffening hand. He unwrapped it and swiftly read it in silence. Then, without looking at his father, he cried out: "This concerns us all—hear it!"

In a loud voice he read it to them all, and when he had ended, fixing his eyes on his father he shouted:

"Is there any man here who will dare after this gainsay this word of the king?" He continued to look fixedly at his father as did they all; and he in the end as though dazed slowly shook his head.

Hakki of Dikkerem came forward to Rolf's side. He was the only one of the younger generation save Rolf who had made the great journey and he now put an arm around him and murmured in his ear. Rolf slowly turned away towards his own men. But when he reached dead Thorburn he dropped on his knees beside him and cast the spear from his hand. As he knelt he placed his gory hands tenderly on either side of the dead man's head and gazed into the quiet serene face, the face of the man who had dandled him on his knees when he was a lonely orphan child, who had taken him out fishing as a boy, and had ever spoken to him as an equal, who had taught him all his fishing lore and seacraft, who had throughout all the perils of the last six weeks shared with him the management of their little boat, so that the two were as the parts of one machine, who even one short hour ago, wet, weary and hungry, had shown a boy's spirit in an old man's body, and had smiled at him as chance offered while the two of them had fought their greatest battle with the sea. And this was his home-coming—slain in the moment of his triumphant return! Great tears coursed down his cheeks—it is a horrible thing

to see a man weep, and men turned away their eyes, while
Hakki silently removed the spear from where it lay.

Bruce, in a low voice, gave orders to his men. They
picked up Kennedy's body, laid it across their muskets and
moved slowly and awkwardly away, southward along the
sands, over the dunes below the little loch and past Milla-
skaera, Edwin and his father, with bowed heads in front,
while the wind still roared around them as though in angry
triumph, and the great rollers crashed in froth and spray on
the sands below. Neither spoke.

Before they faced the upward slope at Voesgrind they
halted for a rest and in the gathering gloom of approaching
night looked back. From where they stood they saw the
islanders move in a crowd upwards past Hooligart, accom-
panying the men from the sea on their way north, this
party also bearing with them their tragic burden. Bruce
heaved a sigh of relief and spoke heavily to Edwin as they
stood a little apart.

"A sair day, Edwin, and but for you it would hae been
waur. There was death in yon mad red-head's een when you
put in an appearance; and we were at a sair disadvantage.
But they'll no get sic a chance again; we maun see to that
noo we are oot o' the wood."

"I cannot see that you are out of the wood, Father. Two
men have been killed and the responsibility lies squarely on
your shoulders."

"Never a bit, man; mind and no let ony ane hear you say
that. If two men hae some private quarrel and ane kills
the ither, and is himsel killed by the slain man's friend,
it's no a matter o' personal concern for me, though in my
official capacity I'll hae to see that the slayer is punished
for takin' revenge intil his ain hands."

With that he gave orders to his men to move forward
once more. Edwin, glancing with a look of pity at the body
being lifted by his comrades, remarked.

"Surely this poor fellow acted on your orders as he

always did; and surely the legal responsibility for his act is yours; *qui facit per alium facit per se* is Scots law as well as Roman."

"Na, na, dinna say that! Rob Kennedy had his ain feuds, nae doot; and, honest man, he canna tell noo what orders he had or had no. Na, it was just a plain case o' thae lawless wild rebels quarrelling among themselves. Never you fash yersel aboot that!"

For a time they proceeded in silence, darkness gathering around them, the one busy with his own schemes, the other very tired (he had had no food for many hours) and chilled too at his father's craft and callousness. When they reached the castle Bruce gave his men orders to carry Kennedy to his own little house not far away, and declared that after a meal he wished to have a talk with Edwin on a serious but not exactly unpleasant matter.

So, more than an hour later, when both were fed and refreshed, Bruce led the way to his own sanctum. Replete with good food and better wine he was in a more cheerful and amicable frame of mind.

"I've been thinking, Edwin lad, that we needna be ower unduly impressed by the royal word, as ye termed it, o' King Jamie. I kent yince an auld Hieland scoondrel that was never greatly fashed at the thought o' retribution for his misdeeds. He used to say: 'Aye, aye, it's a far cry to Loch Awe.' So say I; Jamie may speak o' sending commissions o' enquiry and what no, but it is a farther cry frae Edinburry to the island of Unst. Believe you me, his een are mair directed jist noo Londonwards whaur Queen Lizzie, the auld Jezebel, that took his mither's heid off her shoulders, still hings on tae life and keeps him awa frae the throne o' England. And forbye ony sic orders should hae been gotten frae the Privy Cooncil. It's just his wye o' keeping or trying to keep a' body at peace for the time being.

"But a' that is neither here nor there at the moment.

What I had in mind was something mair personal. The truth is, Edwin, I've been thinking it's time you were married, and what happened to-day has made me mair than ever anxious that you should be settled here to help your auld father among thae lawless scoondrels. Ye've seen to-day hoo they stick at naething."

Edwin was astonished at the turn the talk was taking, and eagerly availed himself of the opportunity of introducing his own views on the matter.

"But, Father, that's the very subject I have been wishing to speak to you about. I have found one here in Unst whom I love with all my heart and——"

"Hoots, boy, listen to what I'm saying and dinna interrupt. Women, you can tak it from me, and saul, I've had some experience and should ken, are just women, some mair sae, some less; but I've no forgotten the daft notions o' the young, and this lass is weel to be seen, has a bit property in land too, and, forbye, weel the truth is, if ye'll no marry her, I'll hae to fix her up wi' Jamie or young Lowrie. Na, dinna interrupt; her father had naething better to do than gang to Edinburry to complain to King Jamie, nae less, against me. He was in yon boat's crew you saw the day; maybe, for a' I ken or for a' I care, the man that Robbie shot. Weel, I heard aboot their ploy through Robbie, and so this morning, as a precaution, ye ken, to stop his mooth if he had made ony impression on the king or the Privy Cooncil wi his tales, I sent and brought the lassie here. She's upstairs in the guest room."

"But, Father——"

"Noo, noo, awa up and hae a keek at her, onyway, man! She's a sousy enough lass; ye'll hae a bit money frae me wi' her, and Helga, Thorburn's dochter, is no empty handed hersel!"

"Helga!" shouted his son, struck as though by a violent blow. He could not think, he could only act. Leaping to his feet, oversetting his chair, and tumbling, as he whirled, a candlestick to the floor he rushed to the door, through the dim hall and up the dark stairway.

"There's no' a' that hurry," quoth Bruce, following more leisurely, candlestick in hand, and chuckling at his son's new found enthusiasm. "Ye need a licht on the dark stairs."

Edwin knocked at the door.

"Helga, Helga!" he cried. "It's Edwin, Helga."

There was no answer, no sound at all to indicate anyone was within. Almost frantic in an agony of love and anxiety Edwin pounded at the door.

"Open, open, Helga; it's Edwin, your Edwin of Valafield!"

"That's nae way to shout at a lassie," reproved his father. "You'll frighten her, man, and, forbye, the door's locked and Marjory has the key."

But even when the key was brought the door refused to open, and finally, impressed by the continued silence, Bruce had the door forced. It was no easy task and required the united efforts at first of two strong men to make the heavy wardrobe and surrounding furniture budge far enough to allow entrance. Then the mystery of the prolonged silence was solved—the open window and the rope of torn sheets and blankets attached to the foot of the heavy fourposter bed and passing out through the window told the tale so far. Helga was gone!

She had soon perceived the possible means of escape and when the boat had been lost to her view, her wits sharpened by anxiety for her father's safety had shown her that escape was vital not only for her own sake but for the sake of her father and her people. Obviously she had been brought here as a pawn in Bruce's game whether with Edwin's consent or not (she earnestly hoped and trusted not). Now if Bruce considered it to his advantage to have her here she must deprive him of that advantage. In any case she must escape! Her father, Rolf, and her friends had ventured their lives for six weeks, cooped in an open boat; were still venturing them, and was she to shrink from a risk that would last only a few minutes at most? Her mind was made up, and composedly she went to work.

She found she had two linen sheets and four woollen blankets to work upon. Together when cut into substantial strips of sufficient width to bear her weight and allowing for the knots they would afford her a rope perhaps fifty feet in length. She began her task immediately. With the aid of a knife from the table (it proved very blunt) she proceeded to construct her rope and the time seemed very long before she finished. Thanks to her experience in little boats with her father and Rolf she knew how to tie knots, she knew there was no danger of them slipping.

In the end she rose to her feet and measured this her clumsy lifeline against her own height. She knew she was a little over five feet in height and this rope was nearly ten times as long. It should serve its purpose!

Resolutely she fastened one end round the massive wooden leg of the bed nearest to the window. Then a thought struck her; the rope might chafe where it passed over the stone window sill. But she solved the difficulty immediately; she would place a pillow between rope and stone. Fortunately the sill projected a couple of inches from the rough stone wall, and with the aid of the pillow the rope would swing clear of the wall a little further so her knuckles should be safe.

What now? It was still too much daylight for her to make the attempt though of human noises she had heard nothing since the party had left in obvious pursuit of the boat. The descent would take perhaps as much as two minutes. Could she hold on so long? She thought she could but she would need all her strength.

At that thought she scanned the table on which food had been set for her. She saw meat, oat cakes, home baked scones, butter, a jug of milk, and of a sudden realised that she was hungry. She seated herself and began to eat slowly and at first not without suspicion. Soon all her fears and caution for the moment laid aside she found, to her surprise, that she was making a good meal.

The roar of the wind around the lofty exposed walls of the castle now never ceased. She looked out and perceived that the sky had become overcast with an unbroken heavy mass of cloud from the north and east, blotting out the light of day. Darkness was rapidly approaching and she deliberated whether to wait until it was completely dark. She knew there would be no moon until late at night; if she did not see the depths beneath her, she might feel safer, but on the other hand she would be more at a loss in finding her way clear of the castle. Gazing down to the ground so far away she planned her route; she would make her way as quickly and silently as she could past the east end of the great peat stack twenty yards away; then keeping it between herself and the castle as long as possible proceed south and west until she thought it safe to turn north. She must descend while there was still enough light for her to descry her direction when she came down. That was if she came down safely—but she firmly dismissed that thought—she knew she would come down without harm.

Waiting a little longer she at last resolutely cast the end of her improvised rope out of the window, but drew it back as a thought struck her. Should she not attach some light weight to the end to make it hang steadier? Immediately she thought of her shoes; she would climb down all the better without them. She removed them from her feet tied them firmly by the laces to the end of her line and lowered away. When all the length was out the line still swayed and she judged her shoes had not quite reached the ground but it could not be helped.

She placed a pillow under the line on the sill to prevent chafing and looked for the last time round the room. The firelight flickered cheerfully on the walls; outside the storm raged. She took a bight of the line between her legs as she

had seen the cragsmen do, thrust her feet over the ledge
and grasping the line below the sill with one hand she held
on to the sill with the other until she had extended her
body to its full length along the line. Then she began her
descent hand under hand.

The wind raved around her and her line swayed a little
and then more and more as she descended. The window sill
gradually receded. Her knuckles grated now and then
against the wall's rough surface but in her excited tense
state she was scarcely aware of that. The knots on the rope
gave her a feeling of comfort, affording her hands a little
rest. She knew she must not look down and finally closed
her eyes. How many knots had she passed? Four at anyrate, and here was five! Then six, then seven; she must be
more than half-way down, eight, and her arms ached and
her left hand did not seem to have any strength now to
grip; nine at last, and she felt herself swinging like a great
pendulum and turning round and round with the rope;
ten, and now there was only one more knot to come;
when that came she would gladly let go for her strength
was gone. Here it was at last, and still she held on, weary
as she was; only another five feet, she told herself, only
another four! Something struck against the back of her
legs. It was the shoes. In a moment, with renewed strength
it seemed, her hands were gripping the line beside them.
No use hanging on now, she thought, and I mustn't leave
my shoes. She grasped them, the slender laces snapped and
she fell.

Or thought that she had fallen, but her feet instantly
touched the ground and she was standing safe. It was only
when she looked upwards at the line swaying white and
ghostly above her and disappearing in the darkness far up
that she felt for a moment a sensation of giddiness. But she
clutched her shoes, ran swiftly and like a shadow round the
corner of the peat stack, sat down, and put on her shoes,
panting the while.

It was not too dark for her to descry vaguely the little loch in front and to the left. She would skirt its western end and keep the stack between herself and the castle. As she started to her feet she heard above the noise of the wind the tread of many footsteps on the stone causeway before the castle entrance, and even the sound of voices. It must be the men returning from their pursuit of the boat, for surely they could not have discovered her escape already. But even if they had not they soon would, and at the thought she sped quietly away.

For nearly a quarter of a mile she hurried, cowering forward, her heart thudding. There was no outcry nor any other sound of pursuit. She paused for a moment and looked back but all was still. Then she changed her direction, and over the dark wasteland, avoiding the haunts of men, past lonely Hellierswater and the stony trow-haunted brakes of Colvadale and Caldback she hastened. Her father would now be at home after his long journey—perhaps, wearied though he must be, preparing to set out to find her. She was sure they had escaped the clutches of Bruce's party —she was sure his mission had been successful! And if it had how they would rejoice together when she arrived! She, too, had played a part in foiling Bruce's plans, plans in which she felt certain her Edwin had had no part. Oh! everything now was going to be all right! In spite of the gale she seemed to speed along, fear of pursuit long since forgotten; in her mind only the joy of homecoming.

At long last Dalsetter was before her, its windows all lighted up. Yes, her father must have reached home!

She rushed in panting, for she had run the last few yards. The house was full of silent, sad-faced men, who looked at her uncomfortably, shuffled their feet, looked at each other, and then stood with their heads bowed.

"Father, where are you?" No one answered and a chill wave of apprehension of a sudden seemed to flood over her leaving her so cold that she shivered. "Rolf, where is my father?" and her voice was so shrill that it jarred on her own ears. Rolf came forward reluctantly, half raised his great hands as though to clasp her in his arms, then, remembering the work in which these same hands had recently been engaged, dropped them to his side. He looked at her piteously like a hurt dog then turned and rushed outside. Mary, the old housekeeper, she who had been first her nurse and, after her mother's death, her second mother and sure refuge in every trouble, came forward and put her arms around her, tears streaming down her kindly withered cheeks!

Over the moors in Muness, Edwin and his father looked around the room, at each other and at the open window with its obvious story, as though they could not believe their eyes. Bruce moved forward and tentatively drew on the rope—it was slack. Edwin rushed from the room as though he were distracted and soon his cries of "Helga! Helga!" from different directions told his father that the prisoner had apparently reached the ground unscathed. He seated himself by the window and waited deep in thought. There was more here than he understood.

Edwin's return was as wild as his departure. "She is gone! Helga's gone!"

"Aye, has she," he replied drily, "and the deevil gang wi' her." He was drawing in the long line of shred blankets and sheets like a dejected fisherman wishing to rebait his line. "Saul, the guid bed-gear ruined like this! It maun a' be cheaper whaur she comes frae. She's gane, ye say. I wish the limmer had cracked her neck in the going. But I might hae taen warning—she was sae quiet—it's aye the quiet yins that are the warst."

He was checked by a rush of words from Edwin, words so bitter and abusive that he almost quailed. He raised his hand in protest but he could not stem the pent up torrent, and found himself listening, at first with amazement and later even with some slight amusement, as his son poured out his tale of love for Helga, of how his affection had been returned, of how their plans and possibly their future happiness had been wrecked by his selfish and callous disregard of everybody's interest but his own, by his abominable interference with other people's lives and rights.

"Weel, weel," he said, more placidly than might have been expected, "I didna think ye had as much spunk in ye, to speak like that to your father or to act as you have done. If spirit coonts for onything ye'll be a bright pair! Oh! its a' right; if ye want the lassie ye shall have her, though, God kens," and he glanced again ruefully at the twisted and coiled line at his feet, "she's likely to prove expensive."

Edwin's rage was unabated. "Can you not understand that she may have another opinion about that, now after the outrageous way in which you have treated her. And worse than that, there's now the blood of one of her own friends between us, maybe even (Heaven forbid it!) the blood of her own father."

"That is so," admitted the older man soberly, "what a pity I kent no a' this afore! But, man, even if the very warst has happened, it was nae faut o' yours; nae faut o' ours I should say," he corrected himself hastily. "The lass will be honourably wedded to ye." Then, as his active mind swept on, removing possible obstacles, he continued.

"Ye'll gang ower the hills to-morrow wi' an escort o' half a dozen lads weel armed in case o' trouble. Tell the lass your father, Laurence the Bruce, asks forgiveness for what was a mistake on his part caused by over anxiety for her welfare. Say he will be prood to hae her as a daughter, and mention of course that he had nae hand nor part in the slaying (which arose oot o' some private tuillye, ye'll say), and that if she consents to marry ye and forget the past, there will be nae mair heard aboot the action o' yon big redheided deevil that butchered Rob Kennedy. If she winna, weel, the law maun just take its coorse so far as he is concerned and ony ithers that had hand or part wi' him."

"No," said Edwin firmly and decisively, for he, too, sore troubled with his thoughts, had made up his mind, "your ways are not our ways. Helga hates them, and so do I. I must settle this in my own way. I shall go alone to see her. If she and her father (if he yet lives) can forgive and she is willing to marry me I shall be very happy. If not, and I feel dreadfully afraid, then I shall leave this place and this land for ever, and never look upon your face again."

He looked at his father as though he would impress his features on his memory and left the room, going to his own; nor spoke to any one in the castle again. For an hour he busied himself in his preparations, donning his best garments, taking with him all the little money and scanty valuables he possessed that could be stowed away upon his person. He had made up his mind; if he failed to win Helga (again his mind was dark with foreboding), he would leave the island for ever, make his way to Scotland and thence to France or the Low Countries, to join whatever band of Scottish mercenaries he chanced on, it mattered nothing which. He must see her as early in the morning as possible.

But he could not rest; in his weary body, his thoughts turned round and round like a wretched bear tied to its stake. Hours passed, and as he found no rest he finally descended the stairs quietly, let himself out by a little postern door, and through the darkness and storm hastened along the route by which Helga had passed a few hours before. The wind howled around him, dark menacing continents of cloud loomed and massed together, occasionally bursting asunder to reveal a fitful glimpse of the cold gibbous moon. Knolls and hollows, burns, peat moors, and stony brakes, wan glimmering waters of little tarns and pools all were passed unnoticed, the wild tumult of the winds matching the equal turmoil of his emotions. It was still dark when he reached Dalsetter, but from one window light streamed brightly forth. He advanced quietly to the window and looked in.

V

Helga sat huddled by the bed on which her father had been laid. Candles burned brightly around him, and a shallow vessel with salt had been placed above the corpse itself. Mary and Sweyn sat with bowed heads a little distance away at the end of the bench by the cold fireside; the other member of the household, Ivar, was in the adjacent room. Thorburn's boat mates, his old comrades, had desired to keep watch round their dead leader, but Helga, who seemed to herself to have turned to ice with no feelings, no emotions left after the dreadful shock she experienced on her return, had firmly refused their offer. To-morrow night, yes, but to-night after their long absence and their exhausting struggle with the sea they needed rest in their own households where they were being so anxiously awaited. So they had gone; Rolf, too, after trying to speak broken words of comfort, after stammering: "I would have died twenty times to save him," and meeting Helga's bleak look as if she neither saw nor heard him, had turned away.

He had talked apart for a little in low tones with Ivar and Sweyn and had then left the house. He had not returned.

So Helga sat. Barely sixteen hours ago she had been happy in her youth, love, and high hope, busied about her household duties, the lark's song in her ear and in her heart. Now after the physical and emotional strains and stresses she had undergone, she was almost beyond feeling and suffering. She looked at times on the calm dead face of her father, at times blankly stared at nothing—she felt as if she, too, were dead.

Edwin entered quietly and with hesitant step as the

light of dawn began to filter slowly into the room, dimming the flickering candles. He went round quickly to the foot of the bed and looked long on the stately immobile face before him and then at the equally still face of his beloved. He called her by name but found he could utter no further word. He moved towards her and his hand wavered uncertainly over her bowed head. Then he knelt before her and chafed and patted her cold hands with his own.

For a time not a word was spoken, but by and by in broken phrases and in low tones he commiserated with her on all she had endured and was enduring. He appealed to her to believe that he himself was utterly innocent and that he, too, suffered with her. When she made no answer he entreated her to say at least that she believed him in this.

"I do believe you, Edwin," she spoke as from far away in some dreadful realm of dreams. "But what does it matter? Nothing matters now!"

Encouraged even at this slight gain, he continued: "But it does matter, darling! We still have each other and our lives before us. My father, when he acted so high-handedly and discourteously towards you, had no knowledge that we even knew each other. He acted to safeguard his own position against men he considered his enemies. Oh! don't think I am defending him. I hate his brutal and remorseless ways. But now he is willing and even eager to have you as a daughter; he has promised and indeed he is compelled to obey the king's command which your father and the other brave men risked so much to obtain. It restrains him as well as all others from such high-handed actions. In future, there will be no more tyranny, no more interference with men's liberties, and you and I, through our union and love, will be able to play a great part in reconciling the parties now so grievously estranged. Your father gave his life for this. Don't let him have died in vain!"

She remained wordless, and he feeling as if he had to continue speaking to dam the dark flood of despair stealing over him went on, raising his voice in the intensity of his feeling.

"Without you, Helga, life holds nothing now for me. If you will not think of your own happiness and mine, think of all the misery that yet may follow for many others. That you hate my father is not to be wondered at, but you and I need never see his face again. He has solemnly promised, too, that if we are wed no further trouble will arise, about the slaying of the two men. He also lost a friend in that mad brawl, but he is willing in that case to let the matter drop against the slayer of his friend. If not he declares he will make the slayer himself and all who abetted him pay the penalty."

Still Helga sat unmoved, but Sweyn who had not been inattentive in his corner by the fireside rose to his feet, and glancing at the set pale face of his mistress left the room.

For a long time there was silence; the candles dimmed wanly in the growing light of morning. At last Helga began to speak, quietly at first and without emotion.

"It's all past now, Edwin! To-day is long ages away from yesterday morning when we were both happy. Whether I love you now or not doesn't matter. I hardly know. But I do know we can never be man and wife. There is between us a gulf that cannot be bridged, a gulf filled with blood. Your father basely murdered mine. I seem to recognise his mean cunning in the words you used about a mad brawl. You and I know that my father would be alive now but for your father's commands. If I could forget everything and start anew, I might consent; but then I would not really be myself, and I must keep my memories. Do you think if we were wed, I could even look upon our bed without seeing what I see now? If we had children would I not look at them in misery, shrinking and fearing ever lest in their features or conduct I should see traces of the mean brutal tyrant so hateful to me, so deadly to my race. No, fate has been hard towards both of us, Edwin, for I know you suffer too. But we do have some freedom of action left, and though I shall never forget you, here we meet and part for the last time. Your life is before you, in a happier land, I hope, and among a happier people; my place is here with my own folk and my own memories. For your father's threat against the man who slew his friend, as he calls him, there are many here who will know how to meet that threat; warn him of that."

Edwin found nothing to say. His own heartache seemed swallowed up in Helga's misery. He rose to his feet, weary and dejected—looked from the dead man to the fair, bowed head of his lost love and turned to leave the room, vaguely and blindly, with no thought of what he should or could do now.

But fate had yet one turn of its wheel for these two distracted and helpless creatures. Ivar, of a sudden, came rushing into the room, startling them all.

"Fly, man, fly for your life, unless you would desecrate this place of death with your own. You will be butchered like a beast! I see Rolf and many others on their way here, spear in hand. Sweyn must have hurried out to tell him you were here."

It was Helga who bounded to the window facing the direction he had indicated. She looked out for a moment. Edwin merely said indifferently: "Let them come. I am weary of it all and would welcome them."

The Helga who turned towards him was not the frozen image of despair he had last addressed.

"Come, Edwin, and you, Ivar, too; we've only the one chance for his life—there's just the one way—come!"

She rushed from the room, out by the back door while the two men followed, as yet not knowing what she meant or why she so acted. Looking back they could see half a mile away up the valley the menacing party advancing in a straggling running line. But Helga was running now in the other direction where the deep Daal of Widwick narrowed steeply down towards the sea.

As they ran Edwin's one thought was to overtake Helga; Helga sped on. She recognised instantly that this was a race for life, his life. She knew that the fierce hate of all his race had now been kindled to a blaze among her father's friends, and especially in the heart of Rolf; she had heard unheeding at the time something of the grim threats that had been uttered as they stood around after bringing her father home. And Ivar, too, knew that death was behind them. He had heard Rolf's raging words that henceforward they would not wait to be attacked but that they would ever be the first to strike, whenever and wherever one of the hated race or his adherents were to be found. He knew it was no empty threat—Rolf had not even waited until Thorburn was buried, but had gone out that very night to lay his plans with the other young hot-heads who were ever eager to follow his lead. Now Sweyn by slipping out to tell him of this poor lad's presence had fairly put the fat in the fire. Ivar well knew where Helga was hurrying—it was to the noost where the little boat lay. If they could reach the boat and push off they would be safe for several hours at least, as there was no other boat for miles along the coast, now that the *Otter* was far away drawn up on Sandwick sands. It was no day for sailing, the wind was still too strong, but once on the water they would be safe.

He glanced back. The pursuers had gained considerably on them. Why should they not; he was not as young as he had been, and these two poor distraught young things were worn out.

Now they were past the turn in the valley and the end of the beach was in sight. By this time Edwin had overtaken Helga and was appealing to her to stop. She gave but one glance back at the pursuers. "For God's sake, Edwin, and for mine, hurry, hurry!" On they went, and the harsh grating of the surf on the rock strewn beach now reached their ears above the sound of the wind. Louder and louder it became as they passed along the burnside until the narrow wick opened out in front of them and they stood by the boat.

Ivar had been overtaken and stood not a quarter of a mile away in the middle of a gesticulating shouting group. There was no time to be lost.

Helga's eyes darted over the gear in the boat, a pair of oars, mast, sail, tiller, rudder, bailer, all neatly in their places, as when she and her father had last used the boat—how many centuries ago it seemed! She raised the aft tilfer, thrust in the plug, away with the shords from the sides, and with Edwin clumsily imitating her efforts the boat was tugged down the steeply shelving beach as though it were reluctant to enter the breaking waves. They were aboard and with a strong thrust of an oar by Helga they were afloat. Only just in time for men were running and shouting scarcely fifty yards away!

Seating herself on the forward thwart she rowed out to sea, the high cliffs on the north side sheltering the wick from the continuous blast of the north-east gale which was still blowing. When the shore was now more than two hundred yards away she ceased rowing, and unrolling the little sail on its yard began to reef it, without even raising her head to glance at the men who now shouted and waved frantically from the fast receding beach.

"We must try to reach Yell, Edwin; there your safety will be assured, and I will not be in danger of falling into your father's hands again; or we can make for the Westing beach where you at anyrate will be safe. What say you?"

"Do as you consider best and safest for yourself, Helga. I have no knowledge of small boats and can help you little, but only tell me what to do and I shall do it."

"When the sail is hoisted the only thing you can do is to keep the water out of the boat as best you can with the bailer. Keep a sure grip of it whatever you do. And do not be scared when the water comes on board but keep on bailing. We are bound from time to time to take heavy lumps on board, and we shall both be very wet, but I'll do my best." She spoke as to a little child or frightened boy.

She slipped the rudder into position and fixed the tiller. It took their united efforts to raise and stay the mast, small and slim though it was, and by this time the shouting from the shore could no longer be heard. She fastened tack and halliards, rove the end of the sheet through the sheet hole in the gunwale aft, hoisted the tiny patch of sail, belayed the halliards and coming aft grasped the tiller and drew taut the sheet.

The sail's mad flapping ceased and the little skiff darted forward like a greyhound after a hare. The great cliffs though now distant seemed to rush past them, the seas breaking tremendously with vast demented roarings on the hidden reefs and shallows, the affrug or backwash so violent that often even the seven hundred feet of Valafield's sombre height though not a mile away was lost to view. The shelter from the cliffs was now gone and they experienced the full strength of the gale. On and on the little boat sped, a tiny world of its own in the midst of chaos. Behind and around them raved the wind and sea, and before them, forgotten and as yet unseen, the *north* tide was roaring and surging fathoms high through the narrow gut of Bluemull Sound almost full in the teeth of the blast.

When Helga did perceive some distance ahead its titanic rage it was too late. The boat unballasted had no chance now of making the swiftly receding shores of Unst; beyond in the distance the spray broke high on the grim black rocks of North Yell and surged on the sands of Breckin, while the mouth of Gloup Voe swiftly opened out. There lay safety, but between was the chaotic weltering maelstrom of warring wind and tide!

Edwin bareheaded and long since drenched, bailed steadily and serenely. To his amazement he found himself smiling, and to his utter joy, Helga, her body taut, shoulder braced against the tiller, both hands straining at the sheet, her hair streaming like a banner to leeward, was smiling back at him, with the smile he had learned to love in the summer sunshine of Valafield's lonely cliffs!

Why follow them further? Three very good seamen accustomed from childhood to battle with the sea in such small boats could have survived perhaps; even two men in such circumstances who knew each other's every thought and action, men like Rolf and Thorburn might have won to safety, but——

When poor maddened Rolf and some of the others at last reached the top of the cliffs on the southern side of the wick and gazed seaward, they saw in the distance every now and then the peak of the little brown sail emerging and disappearing among the billows as the boat struggled on. They saw, too, the ghastly chaos of seas ahead of it, and there came a time when the little sail was swallowed up and rose no more.

When the chief actors in the play have made their final exit, the others can only with more or less awkwardness leave the scene. Laurence Bruce slept long that morning while the wind still howled around his somewhat draughty mansion, and he finally awoke from an uneasy dream in which he had been out in his boat fishing. Instead of an ordinary fishing line he had been hauling long on a line of shred blankets and sheets with never a hook and never a fish until there seemed at last a heavy weight coming to the surface. He hauled and hauled and at last there emerged from the water clear to his view the dead face of the only one of his sons for whom he had ever felt a spark of unselfish affection, and behind, with her long brown hair streaming out like lucky lines, the form and face serenely calm of the wilful lass who yesterday had said: "You will remember this weary day with sorrow for evermore!"

He smiled uneasily as he recalled his dream. "I maun see Edwin after breakfast and arrange things, and I maun send north a party o' men to the funeral to-morrow o' yon dead sea-thief. It'll look respectfu' like and at the same time they'll find oot who the redheided deevil is, whaur he hides, and hoo best to tak him when we want him."

Tradition says that in the church when men had assembled for Thorburn's funeral service there ensued an unseemly brawl. Rolf, catching sight of his hated enemies, assailed, and with his bare hands, mauled two of them so badly that one died from his injuries and the other was crippled. Rolf rushed from the church and no man barred his way. Soon after, not waiting to be seized, he fled from Unst with a few wild followers. Seizing Bruce's own supply ship he became a pirate. In such a profession in those days some men found fame like Francis Drake, or fortune, as Sir Henry Morgan did two generations later; Red Rolf, after many years, so the tale goes, found a hangman's noose in Ireland. That all Bruce's difficulties were not removed by his departure seems indicated in a note by the famous Dr. Jakobssen in his *Place Names of Shetland.* "Changes of -em to -en in the last part (heimer) occurs, e.g., in the name Digeren, a farm in Norwick. In a fragment of a Norn ballad, no longer intelligible partly in Eng. partly in Norn, about the burning of Mooness Castle in the 17th century, a person named Haki o' Dikkerem is mentioned."

But all that is another story. Scarcely now can be seen even a few stones emerging from the grassy mound that covers the rubble of what was once Helga's home, and the mournful winds have soughed through the gaunt roofless walls and blind windows of Muness Castle for more than two hundred years.

7

FEYNESSES AND FANCIES

WHEN the eyes or ears are aware of something that
cannot be explained by the application of ordinary natural
laws, the possessor of the said eyes or ears has seen or heard
a feyness, something that pertains to the realm of the fays
or fairies, and he himself is for the time being "fey", that is,
in possession of supernatural receptive powers. This explanation of the word seems preferable at anyrate to a
derivation from the Greek phaino to show, though as the
expert solvers of cross-word puzzles say, that solution, too,
perhaps merits consideration. Whatever the derivation be,
or whatever their own reality, feynesses have throughout
the ages played their part in the life of man. Take away
Joan of Arc and her feynesses from France and you take
away the mysterious power that set its great heart abeating
and changed the course of history. Or in modern times take
away the efforts inspired and the enthusiasm aroused in the
British people in a very dark hour by the Angels of Mons
in the First World War and twentieth-century history could
have been different.

Feynesses then have had their place in the great wide
world, and they had their place here also in the tiny affairs
of isolated hamlets among the scattered isles. They are (or
were) of course very rare—otherwise they would cease to
be feynesses—and so instances have to be as carefully
searched for as curlews' nests.

All this may serve as an introduction, far too pompous,
to the narration of a few cases of this phenomenon with one

or two remarks thereon. The investigation was undertaken lightly for amusement's sake, it led to conclusions which were one by one abandoned, and it terminated, to compare little things to great, as vaguely as a stream that loses itself in desert sand, or as a Socratic dialogue ending in the usual "here we are, now where are we?" But just as one can dawdle pleasantly enough along the banks of a burn without troubling overmuch where it ends, so let us hope the reader may have a few minutes' pleasure in following our meanderings.

From where we stood in the late February afternoon beside the grey standing stone with the hoary moss of a thousand years upon its venerable head, the village seemed asleep. Round the bay at irregular intervals were dotted the little crofts, many of them now with their whitewashed walls having a dull and wasted aspect as though they were still exhausted and cold from the winter storms. To the south-east beyond the bay and five miles distant the cliffs of Fetlar stood forth in a hazy blue. To geographers and to the natives of Fetlar they are merely the East Neap but to us they are always the Blue Banks, and on a day like this they seemed as ethereal and unsubstantial as a seascape in some Never Never Land of fantasy. Some few seals, basked on the rocks near Fugla Stack half a mile away and the first lapwings of the year wheeled errantly over the moor before us. Beyond and on the height the windows of Oversta seemed to us ablaze as they reflected the light of the sun now low in the south-west above the gloomy hills of Yell.

"You could imagine the whole house to be on fire," said I.

"Yes, very easily," said Gilbert. My ramble in the quiet Sunday afternoon had brought me to the standing stone on my return homewards, and I had found my old friend standing placidly smoking in quiet contemplation, his eighty years as light a burden to him as the burden of fifty to most men. Seaman and crofter and handyman and

P

philosopher he is ready to discuss any subject and to give a very decided opinion thereon.

"Yes," said he. "I remember as a young man the beginning of the tale that Staneshoull was haunted. It arose from just such a light reflection as we are looking at. When the new shop down yonder was opened it had a large frontage of glass, and its four great lamps on a winter night were like a lighthouse. At one point on the beach as you passed east to west along, the Staneshoull windows reflected the light, so that the house seemed all lit up although everyone knew that the owner was away and the place unoccupied. So it soon, without further reason, acquired the reputation of being haunted."

I ventured tentatively. "Most hauntings, I fancy, and tales of ghosts, apparitions and what not, have some such prosaic explanation."

He agreed and for a little we discussed the beliefs of bygone generations. We both admitted that one thing at least they did know far better than we do, even with the advantages of modern science—the probable weather for the coming day or two. The B.B.C. forecasts for the last fortnight had more often than not been almost as far wrong as it was possible to be; to-day itself was an example, instead of a south-westerly gale there was no wind at all.

"As for ghosts," he reflected, "I've never had any faith in them. I don't believe the dead return, but I do know that sometimes you may see a feyness of a living person, but that's nothing. I don't consider that a ghost, just merely a feyness."

"Well, I've never seen even a feyness, but you say you know such things appear?"

"Yes. I remember as a young man coming along the beach from the west as the darkness was coming down. We had been at the store, sorting and mending lines and there were with me your own uncle George and Henry Spence. Well, as we came past Shalderpoint, old Betty

Clarke came out of her house by the roadside and passed us. She was wearing a flowered print dress, carrying her water-bucket in the crook of her left arm, and with her right hand raising the hem of her skirt a little and mincing along in her own affected way. She had been a lady's maid in the south, you know, in her younger days, and had acquired what seemed to us a very mim perskeet manner, even carrying the bucket as though it were a hat box.

"Now she had asked me a few days before to make a kishie (straw basket) for her, and as she passed I said to her: 'I've made what you wanted.' She passed as though she did not hear me, and I, thinking the old lady's getting deaf, turned round, overtook her in four or five steps, and said rather loudly to her: 'I've made what you wanted, Betty,' almost in her ear. She turned round and looked at me but did not answer and swept on.

"We were not far from the new shop, and my friends had entered it when I rejoined them. 'What was the matter?' Henry asked.

" 'I was speaking with Betty,' I said, 'or trying to speak with her.' They said nothing but looked queerly at me.

"You know how it was in the old days; there were no public halls nor recreation rooms, and so the shop was the general meeting place where everyone stood around and exchanged news. Generally it was ten o'clock before shutting time came. The lamps had just been lighted (the same lights I was telling you of that made the place like a lighthouse) and we had not been long in the shop when James Georgeson came in from the westward. When we asked him his news he spoke of the usual things, weather, crops, and animals, and finished by remarking that Betty Clarke was far through and was not expected to live out the night!

"I was amazed. 'Betty Clarke,' I said, 'but I've just spoken to her or tried to speak to her less than half an hour ago.'

" 'Where?' asked he.

" 'Just outside the shop here.'

" 'No,' he said, 'that you did not! She has been in bed in Mucklegirt for the last two days, and is so badly fevered that she cannot be moved. I have just come from there (it was four miles away over the hills) and as for her being out of bed, that, I think, she'll never be any more until she's carried!'

"I turned to your Uncle George and Henry Spence.

" 'Didn't you see me and hear me speaking to her, boys?'

"Your uncle said soberly: 'I heard you speaking but I didn't see or hear anything else.' Henry went very white about the gills. 'Thank God!' he says, 'I heard nothing and saw nothing.' He evidently thought this foreboded some evil for me from which he was safe, but both your uncle and he have now been dead for twenty years and I'm still here. Next morning the postman brought the news from over the hill that Betty had passed away in Mucklegirt some hours after I saw her feyness."

"And even after you heard that news you were still convinced in your own mind that you hadn't made a mistake—you still thought it was Betty you had seen?"

"Yes, I was quite sure it was nobody else."

"I remember," said I, "hearing a story from Willie H—— of Gossawick some forty years ago that had a good deal in common with your story. He was a very straightforward, upright man of sound sense and though he said he did not believe either in ghosts or feynesses, he had himself once and once only seen something for which he could not account. You'll remember him—he was in the R.N.R. about your time."

"Oh, yes, I remember Willie. He went out to New Zealand with his family many years ago."

"Well, he told me that in his youth he was courting a girl some distance away from his own home, and on this

occasion he had set out to visit her at night, but when he
arrived, being a little shy, he decided to wait before going
into the house until the old folk went upstairs to bed.
After waiting a time until he judged by the light that the
old folk had so retired, he was on the point of entering when
a neighbour woman Osla passed the lighted window, and
as he thought (though he could not be certain) seemed to
enter the house. He recognised her quite distinctly and
described to me what she was wearing as he had seen it by
the light from the window. He waited for a considerable
time cursing his bad luck, because he knew she was a great
one for talking, and at last, thinking that she might have
gone out again by the back door, he impatiently went to
the window and peeped in. There was his girl sitting by
the fire but he could see no one else.

"He entered and when Bessie remarked that he was very
late, said: 'I was waiting until Osla went.'

" 'What Osla?' queried Bessie.

" 'Osla W. from Northouse.'

" 'Boy, she's no been here to-night!'

" 'Well, she went past the window at anyrate.'

" 'That was queer,' said Bessie, 'why should she do
that?'

"He did not comment further beyond saying that he had
certainly seen her, and the subject was dropped, except that
when he departed Bessie chaffingly said that she hoped he
wouldn't see Osla again when next he came.

"The following day Osla died suddenly. She had become
ill just about the time that Willie thought he saw her. And
he remained convinced that it was nobody else he had seen.
He described the grey and morrit hap over her shoulders,
the spotted handkerchief she always wore bound tightly
over her head (she was the only person who wore such head-
gear), the way in which she bent a little forward and
plodded as she walked."

We agreed the stories were very similar and after a little

desultory talk about the wet condition of the ground, worse than anyone could ever remember, the prospects of the coming spring, etc., etc., we parted. One cannot draw definite conclusions from two instances, but the stories appeared to have common factors—the light in both instances had been vague; in the one the feyness had been seen before the eyes had adjusted themselves from daylight to darkness, and in the other before the eyes adjusted themselves from the surrounding darkness to the light streaming from the window. The other factor was the foreboding of death for the person whose feyness had been seen.

With a view to the further pursuit of the subject, I was yarning a few nights later with an old lady whose hard battle through life had but mellowed her to a very kindly attitude to every living thing, including a one-legged gull which now for fifteen years had returned summer after summer to perch for scraps on her court dyke—the stone wall enclosing the little space in front of the house. Nellie was quite sure the gull would be returning in summer as usual. The talk gradually came round to the matter on which I wished to obtain information and I finally asked if she had ever seen a feyness.

"No, I never did. I never could believe any of the nonsense the old folk talked. Though there was once I did see something or somebody that maybe wasn't there to see."

With a little persuasion she told the story, content just to leave it unexplained.

Between her home and the post office there was a reasonably good road with a few houses here and there adjacent, and the way itself diversified by braes and hollows and occasional gates. But there was one stretch that always on the return journey appeared rather long and wearisome, for it was uphill in general yet with a long shallow dip that took one out of sight of all houses and of the sea. Well, one night in the darkness, Nellie met a tall woman whom she recognised as Mary R——. She knew her by her height and the very long old-fashioned skirts she wore, but more especially by her grey coat, belted very tightly round her, for Mary even at sixty was enormously proud of her narrow waist. In the village shop one buys all things necessary (or unnecessary) and once a remark of hers had become a temporary byword. After obtaining the usual tea, bread, sugar, etc., she had asked for a pair of corsets and when the young male assistant had briskly asked: "What size?" she had simpered and glancing complacently down had remarked:

"You surely see for yourself!"

The figure passed so quickly that Nellie who meant to ask how Mary's sister was (for she knew she was ill) had not time to utter a word before she passed. She turned round in surprise but there was nobody to be seen, and it was only then that Nellie with a kind of shock realised that it was so dark that she could not possibly have seen what she was wearing, and yet she had seen it.

Hereupon I said: "Now I believe I can tell you the rest of the story. Next day you heard that Mary had died rather suddenly, didn't you?"

"Oh, no, that I didn't. Both Mary and her sister lived for many years after that, but I did find out next day that Mary had not been out of doors the night before, her sister being so unwell."

So one of my hastily formed conclusions had to be abandoned. The appearance of a person's feyness does not necessarily foretell that person's sudden demise. The other conclusion that feynesses need an uncertain light for materialising had to be modified. Apparently feynesses carried with them an aura or light radiance of their own, after the manner of glow-worms, by which they could be definitely recognised even in poor light or no light at all.

I happened some time afterwards to visit another very

old friend who could be relied on to have something to tell from his own experience which might shed light on the subject. I was fortunate enough to find him in talking mood. I broached the subject of feynesses, and said that from all I could hear, they just didn't appear to make sense. They seemed just hallucinations that at undefined times affected the eyes of particular individuals at nightfall or in darkness with little significance either to the person seen or the seer.

On one point he did not agree. Why feynesses should appear at all, and why they should appear to a particular person he did not know, but he did not agree that they were to be seen only at night. From his own experience he could contradict that.

"I've only once or perhaps twice in all my eighty years seen a feyness, and by that I mean something I could not explain at the time or afterwards. I remember that early in the morning after my next door neighbour married I was out and about at the back of the croft before sunrise. It was a lovely autumn morning, and suddenly and unexpectedly my neighbour came walking towards me. He was in his shirt sleeves and had on his wedding waistcoat and trousers. I was surprised but went forward to speak to him and when I was less than ten yards from him he vanished. It was open ground between us and near us and there was no place where he could have concealed himself.

"I considered it very queer, so much so that later on about eight o'clock I called along the house, making an errand about a fence that ran between his land and mine, a fence we had allowed to get into rather a dilapidated state. There's nothing on earth that can lead to such annoyance and petty animosity and squabbling as neglected boundary walls and fences and I thought that now he was married and the real head of the house he and I would get the matter settled, for the maintenance of this fence was our joint responsibility.

"When I came in, his mother was sitting by herself at the fire, and the breakfast things were on the table. I said I had dropped in for a moment to see John. She gave a short laugh and said: 'They're no downstairs yet,' and added some old rhyme about 'newly wed lie lang abed.'

" 'But I saw him,' said I in surprise, 'nearly an hour ago, not far from the south grind.'

" 'Na, that you didn't for I've been up since before six and he's still in his bed.'

"When I assured her that I had seen him as clearly as I saw her, and had been within a few yards of him she said: 'Well, that's good news. It must have been his feyness!' Then she added another old rhyme (she was a great one for old rhymed sayings) something to the effect that 'langs lives he if his feyness ye see in the morning light' and muttered something I didn't quite catch about the sign not being so good in the gathering night. Certainly in this case she proved to be right for John lived to be over ninety."

From this story it would appear that to a previous generation feynesses had sufficient significance for them to differentiate between morning and night appearance and even to have a kind of rule in rhyme about it. I suggested that feynesses must surely have been of more frequent occurrence with them.

"Yes, very likely indeed; life was slower and more deliberate; people with their minds less occupied were more receptive. Nowadays people don't have the time to see feynesses. Young folk and their elders, too, are always in a great hurry to be somewhere else and to be doing something else. They are never in the present—they are always looking twenty yards or twenty minutes ahead."

"You think the feynesses may still be there then, only requiring someone to see them?"

"Why not? We know for instance that the air in this room at this moment is full of the sound of music and talk from a dozen countries, but we don't hear it unless we happen to turn the knobs yonder," and he nodded to the radio set. "In the same way there may be plenty of feynesses about all the time but it is only very rarely that anyone is tuned in so to speak to observe them."

"That does seem possible. And just as radio reception is generally better in the hours of darkness, so it may be with feyness reception. That would account for their appearance in uncertain light, and the fact that the feyness never seems to appear to more than one person at a time would seem to indicate that the tuning in is a matter of chance, depending on some obscure state of the individual's emotions or his optic nerve or both. But you said you had seen a feyness perhaps twice. What about the other time?"

"Well, I don't know that it could really be called a feyness, but if it was you're wrong in thinking a feyness can be seen by only one person at a time. Half a dozen of us saw it.

"It was this way. When the children, some of them, were quite little, we had a large tortoise-shell cat, Spotty, of which we were all very proud. There was not such a magnificent cat anywhere—he was the only tortoiseshell in the island, and a champion fighter. The only cat that could even remotely compare with him in size and beauty was a great white tomcat belonging to the folk of Stoneypark about a mile away.

"You would think there was room for them both at that distance, but na, they had to search each other out, and many a fight they had. That wouldn't have mattered much but their quarrel spread to the boys of both families and as there were five boys in each and all of them at school, and as the other boys, too, were boylike drawn into the quarrel, it was no uncommon thing for us to have black eyes and swollen noses round the table. While the boys admired Spotty for his fighting prowess, among the younger ones at anyrate he was just perfection for his beauty and gentle-

ness with them and when he disappeared great was the
grief and many the search. But he didn't come back.

"One night about six weeks after he had gone we were
all sitting round the table at tea. The lamp had just been
lit, but the curtains had not been drawn across the window.
Suddenly Osla (she was not yet three years old) pointed to
the window and cried out: 'Potty! Potty!' We looked and
there outside on the window sill in his wonted corner
where he used to sit and paw at the window when he
wished to come in was Spotty! We all saw him.

"Ted and Tom jumped up and rushed out to get him and
I was not far behind for I liked the cat nearly as much, I
think, as the bairns did. He must have been scared by our
sudden rush outside for he jumped away from the window.
There was still sufficient daylight for us to see where he
went, and he ran under a fish box that lay on its mouth in
the courtyard. There was a bit broken away from the side
of the box next to us, and the box itself lay clear of the wall.

"We lifted the box, the boys crowding round crying:
'Good old Spotty!' and jostling to be the first to pet him.
Well, you know, he wasn't there, he just wasn't there!
We couldn't believe our eyes; we searched the spot, we
searched all round the yard, and beyond as far as the barn
and byre but we saw him no more!

"Sometime during the next day one of the neighbours
called and said he had found a dead cat lying at the end of
a bank in the peat hill (miles away). He thought it was our
Spotty. The boys went and looked and it was Spotty sure
enough. By the state of the body he must have been dead
for several weeks! They buried it there and to this day they
and I believe that for some reason Spotty came back
several weeks after he was dead. But, of course, that was
not, properly speaking, a feyness, which is an appearance
of a living creature."

"The odd thing is that so many of you saw it, whatever
it was."

"Yes, we couldn't all have been mistaken from the youngest to the eldest, six or seven of us."

"And yet, you know, at a big football match I have heard a thousand voices shouting for a foul or a penalty, although the referee, just one person, disagreed and was probably right in so doing. Numbers are not everything. There you have a thousand persons all seeing something that was not there!"

"That could be, but all the same if all the spectators agreed on what they saw, they would probably be right!"

I thought that that in itself would certainly be a feyness if all the spectators agreed about anything, but admitted that the story of the Cat that Came Back had unusual features—it was really a story more of a ghost than a feyness.

"Na, well, for a real ghost story, you would have to go farther back even than my generation. My grannie, (she was a woman from the Mainland), had some wonderful ghost stories that made us creep closer to the fire and Dad's old Orkney chair in the winter nights, when the wind was roaring abune the rafters and down the chimney. All my life I've never been at a wedding but I felt a grue that I can trace only to one of her stories."

"It must have been a powerful tale to leave such an impression."

"It was indeed, but nobody could tell it like Granny, for she had known, so she said, old people who could remember about the strange occurrence. I can give you just the bare outlines."

Thereupon, when his pipe was drawing to his satisfaction, and everyone was suitably silent and expectant after due cogitation he proceeded with the story of the Invited Skull.

"Sinnie o' Nedderdaal was as handsome a lass as anyone could wish to see, and as she was the only child of a very well-to-do crofter she did not lack for suitors. Although she was in no hurry to make up her mind, by and by everyone in the district saw that her choice would rest on one or other of two young men. Eric Thomason of Wasterknowes was a dark, quick-eyed, powerful young seaman, open-minded and open-handed, going to the Greenland whaling in spring and summer, and to the line fishing in autumn. He was nimble, fearless and sure in a boat, a fine seaman, but restless and a bit reckless on land, and was rather fond of a dram—poor fellow, as it turned out. Olaf Sweenson was in some ways his opposite, fair, quiet and composed in manner, a bit reserved and deep. His father had a shop and did a good trade, for he could be relied on to satisfy his customers; if he did not have in stock what was wanted he knew where to get it. But it was Olaf who was his mainstay. Olaf knew everybody and was in touch with everybody, and, knowing all the smugglers foreign and native alike, he kept the shop well supplied with liquors of the best, silks, and suchlike that had never paid duty.

"Sinnie, after a little backing and filling, saw she would have to make up her mind between them or run the risk of losing both, for the two young men were good friends, and they had asked her bluntly to choose between them. On serious consideration she reckoned Eric undependable, uncertain, a bit reckless and too fond of drink; Olaf was reliable, had, or would have, a good business, and was quiet and even-tempered. It would be the sensible thing indeed to choose Olaf. No one then was surprised when after such considerations she chose Eric—women are made like that!

"So you must picture Eric setting out over the hills to the manse to arrange with the minister to make proclamation of the coming marriage. With him was Olaf who was to be his best man. As they went in the gathering dusk Eric was in high spirits—he had imbibed freely and had insisted on Olaf drinking too. The churchyard lay in their path and Eric, with a laugh, vaulted over the low wall and said: 'We must take every short cut to-night.' Olaf followed reluctantly. There was a bit of a moon; it was a few days

old, and as they went Eric struck his foot against something
that gleamed in the uncertain light. He stooped and picked
up a skull which had been thrown up from a newly dug
grave.

"'Ha, ha! old chap,' he cried, holding it in his hand.
'I've got more to grin at than you. Here,' he said in
serious tones, 'do you know this, I'm getting married soon
to the best girl in the whole world.' Olaf was shocked.
'Stop it, Eric, you're speaking to the dead! No good can
come of such a thing.' 'What?' shouted Eric, and Olaf
said afterwards he looked as if he were 'fey'. 'Here, I'll
show you if I'm scared of a dead skull or no.' He held it
up so that the great eye sockets seemed to look into his
face. 'You,' he shouted, 'whoever you are or whoever you
were, I invite you to my wedding at Nedderdaal on the
twenty-first of this month. Mind, you're one of the friends
of the bridegroom, Eric Thomason—just ask for me, and
mind and come!' As he spoke there was a shrill peal of
laughter from beyond the churchyard wall, and he hastily
dropped the skull.

"After a little silence he said: 'That made me jump. Do
you know I thought it moved in my hand. But yon's just
fule Robbie—he's been watching the gravedigger—he aye
does.'

"The moon was not yet full when over the hills at
Nedderdaal the wedding was in full swing. The guests,
arm-in-arm, had returned from the church, been wel-
comed, with the fiddlers' Farther Ben the Welcomer and
with a dram and a substantial meal, while many a toast
and many an expression of good will had followed; the
bride's reel had been danced, and the fiddlers exuding
perspiration and good spirits were playing Kail and
Knockit Corn while old and young alike crowded the
floor in a Shetland reel. Within all was brightness and
good cheer, outside a strong wind had arisen and was roaring in increasing violence, while dark clouds had swept the

moon from the skies. Under an extra heavy gust the door blew open with a crash and a tall man clothed all in black and with a dark mask over his eyes stood in silence surveying the scene. The utter blackness of his garb, the deadly pallor of the portion of his face visible, and his motionless silence swiftly drew all eyes. One by one the dancers stopped and a chill for which the open door was not entirely accountable passed like a wave over them. Those who stood nearest said afterwards it was as if a great frosty candle (an icicle) had stood among them.

"'I would speak with the bridegroom, Eric Thomason,' The words came slowly and almost uncertainly from the pale lips. Eric jumped forward and the figure turned and went out of the door which no one had had the thought to close—so strangely had they been affected. Behind him went Eric from the eyes of men.

"No one of all the happy throng ever saw either of them again. And yet that is perhaps not quite true. At the wedding was little Willa Hendryson, four years old. Her mother was sister to the bride's father, and with her husband and little girl had come from town for the occasion. Willa afterwards could remember the noise and jollity of the wedding, the bright lights, the enormous heaps of good food, the huge size of everyone and her own smallness. She could not of course recall the uneasiness and finally the alarm that spread among the guests for by that time she was asleep. Nor did she know of the more and more hopeless search conducted day by day for many weeks. Nor did she know until long after of the story told by 'fule Robbie', and reluctantly supported by Olaf, of the incident of the skull.

"Forty years later, Willa, now with a husband of her own and a daughter Mary, was staying in what had been her uncle's house in Nedderdaal. He was long since dead, and Sinnie after mourning for Eric for two years had wed Olaf and they now had a thriving business in one of the big cities of the south to which they had gone shortly after their marriage. They still owned Nedderdaal and kept the house in good repair, letting it at times to chance visitors or to Willa and her family, although they themselves scarcely ever made use of it.

"Mary, a bright pert lass of fourteen, was adjusting her curls and admiring herself in a small hand-mirror one autumn evening when someone came to the door and without knocking, entered. It was an old bent man, his mean clothes wet and mudstained, his hands and face smeared and dirty.

" 'What do you want?' she cried sharply. "Why didn't you knock?' for she was used to town ways.

" 'Where's Sinnie and where's all the folk?' the stranger croaked.

" 'What folk?'

" 'The wedding folk, and Sinnie and everybody.' He looked around and impatiently drew the back of his hand across his eyes.

"Mary's nerve cracked; she wasn't afraid of an old man but she was afraid of a madman, and she cried out: 'Mam, Mam, come here, quick!'

"Her mother heard her and hurried in from another room. 'Here's a man wanting to know where the wedding folk are,' and big lass though she was, Mary took up position behind her mother.

" 'The lass is a fool,' the old man said. 'I merely asked for Sinnie and the wedding folk. Who are you anyway?'

"Willa stared. 'There's no Sinnie or wedding folk here,' she said. 'This is Nedderdaal. You must have come to the wrong place.'

" 'I know this is Nedderdaal. I should know where my own wedding is. Where's the wedding folk and Sinnie? Where's everybody?' And as he saw the expression in their eyes, his voice rose to a shriek: 'The folk that were here yesterday,' and then in a lower tone and with a kind of entreaty: 'Or the day before yesterday maybe, or the day before that?'

" 'There's been no wedding here,' said Willa, awed by his manner. 'Not a wedding here for forty years, not since the wedding of Sinnie Waterson and Eric Thomason.'

" 'Are you mad or am I mad?' and he took a step towards them. But his eyes fell on the hand-mirror Mary had laid on the corner of the table before the window. He picked it up, looked into it, then drew his left hand first over his face then over the surface of the mirror, then he held it beside Mary's pale face which was thrust forward in speechless amazement. When he saw that the mirror gave a true reflection, he let it fall limply from his hand, stood for a moment as though turned to stone, then turned and was gone without another word.

"Mary gazed at the shattered glass on the floor. 'That's seven years' bad luck,' she said as if she scarcely knew what she was saying. Her mother was swaying on her feet. 'Maybe someone has had more than seven years' bad luck!' she said, and fainted away.

"But if it was Eric who had come back, no one else saw him again either then or afterwards.'

There was a pause when the old man finished his tale. When no one made any comment he continued: 'Can you wonder that I have always at weddings an uncomfortable feeling that the door may open . . . and can you explain in any natural way all that happened in this tale of my granny's?"

One had the impression that, curious though it may seem, the whole story was probably true, that these events had happened so, and at least two explanations suggested themselves, both unpleasant, but at anyrate more probable than that a skull should clothe itself in human form and garb for the purpose of attending a wedding and abducting the bridegroom. Fortunately a very cogent reason kept one silent.

By my venerable friend's fireside in the chair of honour
sat a chum of his boyhood days—old Geordie, the big
strong hands of him nearly as capable still as they had been
more than forty years ago when in the gathering gloom of a
stormy April night he had brought his little fishing smack
and her crew safe to harbour nearly twenty-four hours
after all hope of her safety had been abandoned in the
great gale. His bald shining head gleamed intermittently
in the smoke of his Bogie Roll—his bright eyes danced; and
when he hawked twice in his throat, it was unnecessary to
bid the initiated to give attentive ear. Two things Geordie
loved, a game of euchre, and an exchange of yarns and old
tales with his cronies, and throughout the following narrative while he spoke his whole body was astir with little
movements of knees and hands and shoulders as if the
liveliness of his thoughts had to find expression in more
than words alone.

"None of you but John here will remember Peter
Williamson and Baabie his wife, who lived at Lower
Collaster in their little croft midway atween the cliffs and
the steep side of Brettafield. For some years they had
lived all by themselves; the family had all grown up and
dispersed over the face of the earth, and the youngest,
Tammy, who had remained at home, when he was on the
point of marrying and taking over the croft had fallen over
the cliffs and been killed. Well, for a time they managed
just as many others have done before them, and after them,
but in their case something unusual did happen.

"Peter had a brother Robert who had gone away to sea
when he was a boy of seventeen and he had never returned.
Now and again a letter or news of him would reach home—
he was a sailor and very much of a rolling stone, and the last
that had been heard of him was that he was in Australia
and at the gold-diggings. But that was years ago, and he
was believed to be dead when a letter arrived from him
saying that he had made, not a fortune, but more than

enough to keep them all comfortable for the rest of their days, and that, as he had no ties in Australia, he would like to come home and settle down in peace once more, and see the sun set in the western sea beyond the Wasting holms as he had done so long ago. If Peter could put him up in the old homestead that would suit him; if not, could he stay with him until he had a house built for himself?

"Well, well, you can imagine how Peter felt. Forty-three years is a long time and one changes in many ways, but Robbie was his brother, and Peter's feelings were as kindly and almost protective towards him as they had been when his strong restless younger brother had last looked into his eyes and shaken him silently by the hand so many years ago.

"So when Robbie arrived it was between them as if he had never gone away; that is so far as kindness was concerned. As for protection, Robbie needed none. He was a big, black-bearded, broad-shouldered giant, dressed in what seemed a rather flamboyant, flapping style with a large slouch hat, and a bright-red silk muffler the most conspicuous parts of his attire at a distance; though when he stood in all his breadth before you, you couldn't take your eyes off his gold watch-chain and the gold nugget that dangled from it; as his brother said laughing, it was big enough almost to be the chain and anchor of a sixern.

"He was noisy, open-handed and friendly, and when he yarned in his tremendously deep voice about Ballarat and Bendigo, and the Timor Straits, the cannibals of the Solomons, about the bush and the Black Ned Kelly the bush ranger, he had everyone gaping in amazement. He had actually been held up with half a dozen other miners by Kelly himself. At that time he was fresh to the diggings and his little leather bag had at most about two ounces of dust. Kelly had tossed the bags of the other fellows to his henchmen but dandled Robbie's in his hand two or three times and had then thrown it back to him with the remark: 'See me in five years' time, digger!'

"Now it had been late in October when Robbie arrived. He had joined in all the hard work of the harvest, had busied himself outdoors and indoors, was on excellent terms with Peter and more important still with Baabie, and he had great plans for what he and Peter would do to the house in spring. Christmas Eve had come round and the weather had been fine, and early in the morning he declared he was going to visit Charlie Peterson who had been his boyhood pal and who lived five miles away over the hills at Pettester. So far he had not found time to do much visiting but he must visit Charlie to-day for old times' sake.

"Baabie and Peter both protested. Baabie was disturbed by the heavy seas on the holms. She averred bad weather was not far away, and it was a wild lonely road which in one place ran close under the steep side of Valafield and the awesome 'banks' (sea cliffs) where poor Tammy had met his fate. Peter, too, doubted the weather —he noticed the mares were beginning to gather at the north side of the croft in a hollow to leeward of a protecting wall. And it was Christmas Eve; could he not wait till after Christmas?

"Robbie laughed. He promised solemnly to be back by midnight at the latest, and as for weather, well—he reckoned he was still fit enough to deal with that.

"There is no road, of course, hardly even a footpath but, all the same, it's a fine walk on a summer day—along by the Ness and the Keostines, past Longa Geo and Hagdale's Ness and up and up along a path nearly as steep as a stair, the great cliffs rising ever with you and close to the left hand until you look down at the seas breaking round the South Holms and the foot of Sinna Stack hundreds of feet below. Even on this winter day it was a grand walk, and Robbie paused at last on the Knowe of Tronamires, and as he gazed first to westward where the lively sea stretched to the horizon, unhampered and unfettered as he knew for

thousands of miles all the way between himself and Greenland, and then to the east where the long voe of Baltasound slept in winter sunshine and calm, with the blue peat
reek rising from a hundred homes, he felt as it were the
wings of youth sprouting on his shoulders. It was fine to
be home again!

"And what a reception he had at Pettister! Charlie, the
laughing cheery friend of his boyhood was now a grey-
bearded grandfather, and his house was full, or seemed to
be full, of grown sons and daughters, with their mates and
children. And don't forget Charlie was a Peterson! Fine
hands and mastery of the fiddle and a cheery heart are
God's gifts to all the Petersons. Robbie was overwhelmed
with kindness, music, and good cheer, and while he found
the company much to his liking, so they found him so
congenial, and so fascinated were they by his personality
and his talks, that they all shouted in protest when at eight
o'clock he rose to his feet and said he must take the road.
They would not hear of it, he must stay the night or better
still, stay a week or two.

"But Robbie was firm. 'No,' he said, 'I promised I'd be
back by twelve at the latest. Out in the wilds, where I've
been all my life, a man does many things he should not,
but one thing he never does—not a real man. He never
breaks his word.' He swept away all their protests, that
it would be all right, that Peter and Baabie would not
expect him back, that the weather was not looking good,
and with many a promise of a speedy return set out.

"The weather had changed and the wind was blowing
quite strongly from the south-west. Dark clouds piling up,
mass on mass, soon blotted out the week-old moon and it
was bitterly cold. Long before he reached the knowe of
Tronamires and the top of his ascent Robbie had slackened
his pace considerably, and he paused for a little before
beginning the steep descent. He would have to go slowly;
in the darkness a false step might plunge him into one of

the deep rents or holes in the peat moor, rents and holes so narrow and so deep that even if he escaped a broken limb he might not be able to extricate himself; and if he went just a little too far to the right and his foot slipped, he would be over the four hundred foot precipice before he knew, for there was neither protecting wall nor fence.

"He began the descent, but before he had gone a quarter of a mile he was in the midst of a mad blizzard of roaring wind and blinding snow. Soon they met him in such force that he felt as if he were trying to walk through a haystack. But he was unafraid. 'Gently does it, old lad, gently does it,' he kept on thinking to himself, adjusting his pace to the slow pump, pump, pump of his heart which he began to feel. He was after all not so young as he had been, but he remembered being lost in the bush for forty-eight hours, and he had saved himself by keeping his head. Turning his back to the wind he adjusted his muffler over nose and mouth, tucked his head down until he felt the comfortable pressure of his beard on his chest and plodded on and on. Please God the wind would keep steady in the south-west; in the roaring choking darkness it was the only compass he had to steer by, and if it went more westerly he would walk over the cliff and that would be that!

"Now and then a gust more powerful would bring him to a full stop, and many a time he had to turn his back and adjust his muffler which kept slipping. Gradually he became aware of himself as something solid and white moving through a roaring formless void. 'Slowly, slowly, but keep moving, keep moving' over and over again the thought slid itself into a kind of rhythm by which he moved. He reckoned he must now be near the steepest part of the way down, for although he knew his progress could hardly be a mile per hour, yet he seemed to have been already a long, long time on the way, a long, long time, but slowly, slowly, keep moving, keep moving!

"Without warning he felt himself falling forward, falling

slowly, the wind bearing him up; his head was lower than his feet, he rolled over, his shoulder jarred, he lay face downwards flat on the ground. And what was this? The wind was blowing so fiercely *up from the earth* that his head was tilted backwards with its force! For a little he remained as still as death, as he realised that he was lying on the very brink of the precipice with his head actually projecting over the cliff. As if he had found himself lying face to face with a sleeping tiger he began to creep backwards, inch by inch, slowly, slowly, quietly, quietly, until he felt himself at a safe distance. Even then he was reluctant to rise to his feet, he was warm and tired, and, close to the ground, the wind had lost some of its intensity. He was tempted to lie still, it was madness to proceed with the cliff so near, the blinding snow could not last for ever, and surely the wind could not blow with such fearful intensity for any length of time. Why should he strive further?

"But he remembered his promise. He had promised Peter he would return that night, and it was good old Peter that, as a boy, had taught him to keep his word. Grand times they had had as boys, and if he lived they would have grand times again. But he would not live if he lay here! With that thought he stumbled to his feet and faced his enemies the wind and snow again. He had not much strength left, and decided that he must change direction a bit, taking the wind and snow rather on his right cheek; that should at anyrate take him away from the cliffs.

"He plodded on slowly, slowly, very slowly, stop! With many such pauses he nursed his fading strength, raising his head ever so little now and then, and through half-frozen eyelids seeing always nothing but the raging mad grey flurry of the elements. If only he had shelter for five minutes his strength might yet come back, but he felt it now at every step to be ebbing, ebbing away. The snow was now very much deeper; for a time he had been wading

above the knees. He fell forward and lay half buried.
There didn't seem much point in rising again, but after a
little he did so. The wind and snow had gone! There was
only a blackness before him and he put forward his hands
groping. He touched a stone wall which towered above
him. He tried a little way to left and right and realised he
was standing under the shelter of a gable. Memory flooded
back and with memory hope. It was the croft of Outer
Clave, it had to be; for there was no other house in all the
way or anywhere near his path; he had saved his life, for
with Lowrie and Jean he would be all right in ten minutes'
time! Passing to the right round the corner he saw what he
expected—the glorious light shining through the ben
window on the whirling snow.

"He almost fell as he entered, but with an effort managed
to stand. Lowrie's great sailor voice boomed: 'Come in,
come in, whoever you are; boy, boy, what a night!' and
round Lowrie's elbow came Jean, old and bowed but sharp-
eyed as ever. 'Oh! it's Robbie,' she cried. 'Robbie!' and
her old fingers fluttered at his muffler, untying it; and
'Help him off with his coat, Lowrie,' and while Lowrie did
so, she thrust the teapot close to the blazing brands of a
fine peat fire. Robbie, before he knew, was seated in the
large commodious cane chair he remembered so well.
'Here's a dram, while the tea draws.' Lowrie had stepped
to a little cupboard in the wall by the chimney neuk and
taken out a stoneware jar. There was a musical gurgle as
he filled a cup and pressed it to Robbie's lips. The fiery
liquor made Robbie gurgle too; life ran through his body
until he felt his big toes throb and tingle. He stirred and
looked around—the blazing fire roused by Jean's kindly
restless hands gave forth most of the light in the room;
a flickering collie lamp on the window-sill supplied the rest.
The roar of the wind in the chimney was continuous, but
dulled like seas breaking on far off sands. As Lowrie
moved away to get fuel from the peat neuk Robbie descried

a young man seated on a bench by the window. The lad gave him a friendly smile but said nothing.

" 'You mustn't make tea,' Robbie was feeling very much revived. He hurriedly told the story of his journey and concluded. 'I'll have to hurry home as Peter and Baabie will be frantic with fear for me till I come. I promised I'd be back to-night. No, you must excuse me this time, and I'll promise to come and see you soon—that I will.' Lowrie protested vehemently but Jean like all small women took the opposite view. 'Maybe he's right, they will be sore frightened. But Tammy here will follow you; well he knows the road; he's no a great one for speaking, but he aye likes to be doing something.'

"Soon once more, Robbie faced the gale and the blinding snow, but at a quicker pace and with the comfort of the strong young man beside him. Even if they had wished to talk, it would have been impossible, but there was always the friendly touch and slight jostle at his elbow. Even so, by and by Robbie found the slowly, slowly, keep moving, keep moving rhythm again, beating, it seemed, in his head, which felt so stiff he could no longer raise it. Suddenly his comrade grasped his arm and pointed. With an effort, Robbie raised his head a little. The light streamed forth from the window within six paces of him. Tammy raised his hand in a gesture of friendship and farewell turned round and was gone. Robbie opened the door and stumbled in.

" 'Providence be blessed!' cried Peter. 'Oh, Robbie, Robbie, man!' and he struggled with his coat, for Robbie's beard was frozen stiff to the cloth. At last he was seated in the Orkney chair, Baabie struggling to get off his boots, and almost crying with relief. 'It was all our fault, we should never have let you go—anyone could see bad weather was coming.' Peter pressed to his lips a generous measure of rum and stood over him until he had swallowed it all. 'Sit you still, don't speak a word until you have had some food.' Nor would he allow him to say anything until they had all partaken of the supper which had been waiting so long.

"The men folk lit their pipes, Baabie began tidying away the supper things. 'Gosh I am tired,' said Robbie yawning. 'I think I'll off to bed. It's the hardest struggle for life I ever had, and if it hadn't been for the folk at Outer Clave I sure was a goner.' 'What folk?' said Baabie. 'Lowrie and Jean, of course.' Peter uttered an exclamation and jumped to his feet. 'So, come on, we'll hear the rest in the morning, you're tired, you're tired, lad!' and putting his arm around him led him off to bed.

"Breakfast was very late in the morning. Twice Peter had looked in on the sleeper and twice had tiptoed away. Now the three were seated at table, Robbie still weary and contented just to sit and toy with his food, the others unusually silent. At last Baabie with an effort at brightness, said: 'How were all the Petersons?' And Peter added: 'Yes, but take your time. Man, you must have had an awful night! It was the worst storm I can ever remember; the wind and snow did not slacken until daylight came in.'

"Robbie began his story and told it well in all its details. If he had looked up he would have observed Baabie's old face grown pale and her hands shake, until she suddenly gave a little cry and sat back in her chair, her eyes full of tears.

" 'Stop, Robbie, stop, for mercy's sake,' cried Peter, but Baabie screamed: 'Let him go on, you fool, don't you understand?' and, turning to Robbie, she entreated: 'Oh, you must go on, Robbie, you must or I'll die.' Looking in surprise from one to the other, he hastily brought his story to an end.

"There was a long silence. Baabie and Peter had gazed at him, then at each other a long, long time. Then Peter began hesitatingly: 'Robbie, when did you last see Lowrie and Jean, I mean before last night?'

" 'Just before I went away.'

" 'Yes, but, Robbie, that's forty-three years ago, forty-three years!'

" 'So it is, so it is!' said Robbie, then as a thought struck him he stammered: 'They have worn well, they were just as I remembered them.'

" 'Lowrie and Jean,' said Peter slowly, and he stretched out his great hand and laid it over Robbie's protectingly, 'Lowrie and Jean have both been dead for nearly twenty-five years; they died within a week of each other in the year 'sixty; the very roof has been off the house for twenty years!'

"Robbie sat as if he had been turned to stone; a greyness spread over his face; his lips moved, but no sound came. Peter rose from his seat, walked round the table, and hugged him tight as he had done long time ago when his little brother hurt had looked to him for comfort. 'It's all right, Robbie, you came through a storm where many a man thirty years younger would have perished. But you were nearly all in just before you reached the house, and you just imagined the last part!'

"But here Baabie broke in. 'He did not, he did not!' she said passionately. 'It was Lowrie and Jean he saw, and Tammy too, my Tammy!' and she rested her head on the table and sobbed. Peter stood between them, still resting one hand on Robbie and with the other stroking Baabie's hair, once golden but grey now ever since that dreadful morning six years ago when Tammy in his youthful strength had passed from them so suddenly.

" 'It was Tammy!' she cried. 'Oh, Peter! You're blind. Do you not remember how Tammy, when a little boy, used to go and spend a week-end now and then with Lowrie and Jean? And do you not remember the very last time you and I were there, when I said to Jean I hoped Tammy had been a good boy, she said: "We are aye glad to have him; he's no a great one for speaking but he aye likes to be doing something"—just the very words she said to Robbie last night!'

"Outside, the snow lay deep, nearly three feet deep on level ground, with the drifts in places six or eight feet more. It was three days later, when Robbie and Peter in their search for missing sheep found their steps turning northwards, and the wintry sun was on the point of dipping into the western sea, when they stood before the bleak walls of Outer Clave.

"The. gables still stood but the lintels had fallen from windows and door, and byre and barn were but a confused hummock of rubble covered with a mantle of snow. Without a word, without looking at each other, they entered through the gap which had once been a doorway. Within, the snow was quite deep towards the south end, but wind eddies had kept the north end fairly clear. The bare wall and the empty fireplace with its cracked lintel stone stared back at them. In the gable wall in the corner to the left of the fireplace was a bare stone recess about two feet high by a foot in width and depth. It had served as a humble cupboard to Lowrie and Jean long, long ago, and there on the gaunt pitiful stone they saw, carefully laid, and neatly folded, Robbie's red silk muffler!"

When Geordie had thus brought his tale to its conclusion, there was silence, as Macaulay says, while men might count a score. The unspoken question in his bright eyes was not so easy to answer. A threefold cord is not easily broken, and to explain away naturally Lowrie and Jean, *and* Tammy, *and* the red silk muffler would certainly require a considerable effort! Unless, of course, one fell back on the opinion once expressed by an old Dutchman to an American who, after spinning a terrific yarn, had asked him: "What do you think of that?" The Dutchman meditated profoundly and then said: "Ah tank it vos von big lie!"

But one could not say that to Geordie, not when one regarded his benevolent bald dome, his patriarchal beard, and the great gnarled hands of him in whose keeping men's lives had been so safely held before we were born. No, as Chaucer has it: "There nis na more to say"; Geordie had brought his boat safely to anchorage once more!

APPENDIX

WHALES AND WHALE HUNTING

Diodorus Siculus de gestis Alexandri (*circa* 20 B.C.). Macedones narrabant in multa et incredibilis magnitudinis cete se incidisse, unde consternati spem omnem vitae abjecerint, quippe qui arbitrarentur viros omnes una cum navibus ab illis subito absumptum iri. Sed postea animis resumptis clamorem magnum omnes se pariter edidisse, simulque armis collisis et personantibus tubis tantum sonitum fecisse ut perterritae beluae subter aquam se demerserint.

Oppianus in the Halieutica (A.D. 160) according to Gellius and Conrad Gesner. Extracts.

Esca est jecur aut scapula tauri. Tum tacite remigantes nutu si quid opus est significant, et summopere cavent ne ullo sono percepto bellua in profundum refugiat. Haec ut escam videt nulla cunctatione interposita effreni aviditate eam appetit atque statim ferro ejus guttur transfigitur. Cujus dolore incitata, catenam exedere et conficere conatur: quod ipsum postquam diu multumque conata est, acerrimis doloribus affecta, in pelagi profundum demergitur. Tum omnem funem huic relaxant, quod nullis humanis viribus retrahi possit et facile exagitata fera navem cum remigibus in profundum detraheret; simul et amplos utres venti plenos ex funibus belua mare subeunte appendunt——

Tandem alii hastis seu jaculis, alii tridentibus, alii securibus falcibus aliisve instrumentis armati caedunt, utcunque renitentem statuque cientem procellas: et

254

vulneribus quibus inflictis mare rubescit, putridam senti-
nam infunduntacrem et ignis instar mordacem——

Othere's story (*circa* A.D. 880) inserted by King Alfred
in his translation of Orosius.

Othere saede his hlaforde Aelfrede cyninge thaet he
ealre Northmonna northmest bude.—On his agnum lande
is se besta hwaelhuntath: tha beoth eahta ond feowertiges
elna lange, ond tha maestan fiftiges elna lange; thara
he saede thaet he sixa sum ofsloge sixtig on twaem
dagum——